Editor
Jenni Corcoran, M. Ed.

Illustrators
Mark Mason
Kelly McMahon

Cover Artist
Brenda DiAntonis

Editorial Project Manager
Mara Ellen Guckian

Managing Editor
Ina Massler Levin, M.A.

Creative Director
Karen J. Goldfluss, M.S. Ed.

Art Production Manager
Kevin Barnes

Art Coordinator
Renée Christine Yates

Imaging
Nathan P. Rivera

Publisher
Mary D. Smith, M.S. Ed.

Author

Stephanie Lester

Teacher Created Resources, Inc.
6421 Industry Way
Westminster, CA 92683
www.teachercreated.com

ISBN: 978-1-4206-8770-5

Reprinted, 2008
Made in U.S.A.

Table of Contents

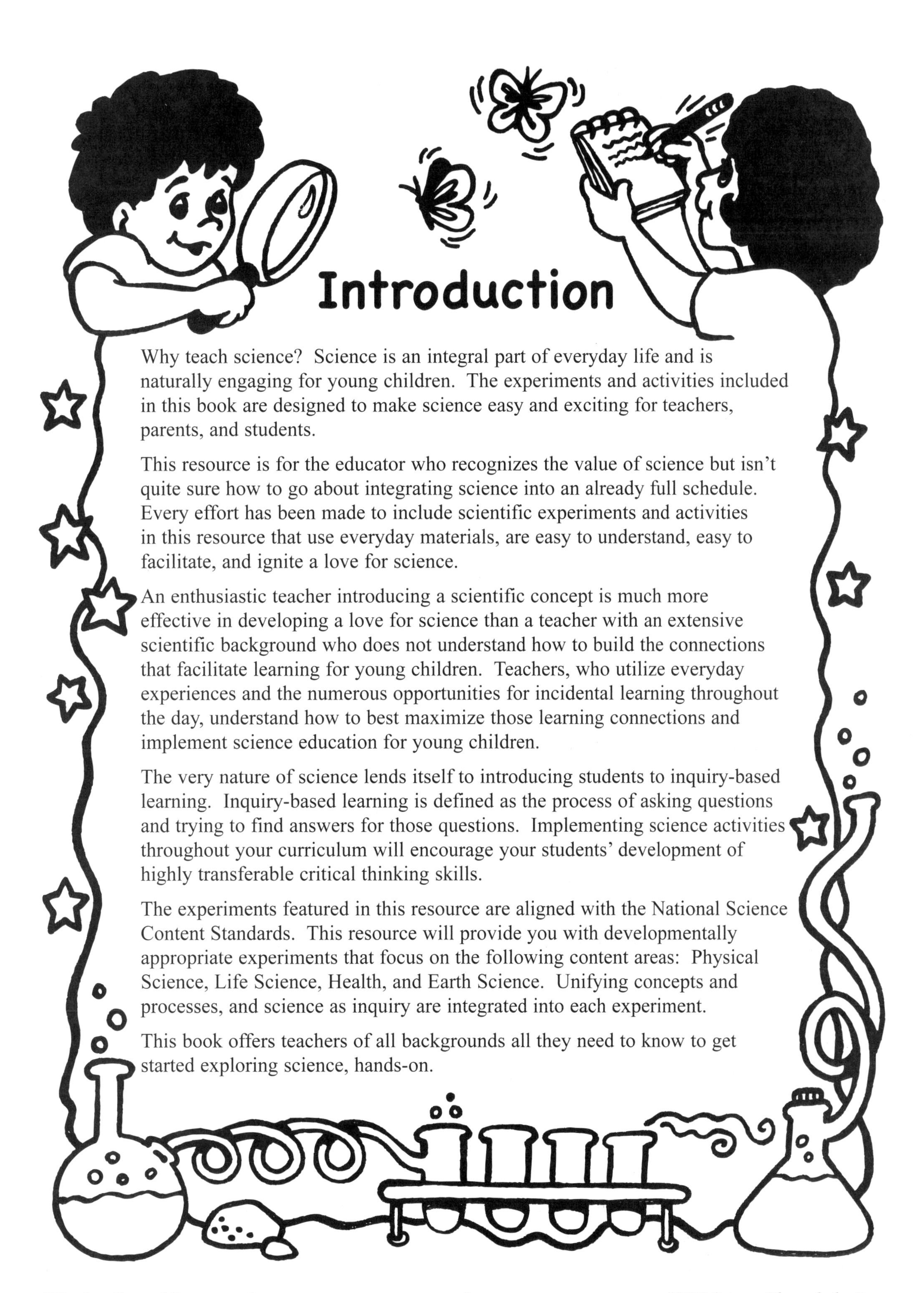

Introduction

Why teach science? Science is an integral part of everyday life and is naturally engaging for young children. The experiments and activities included in this book are designed to make science easy and exciting for teachers, parents, and students.

This resource is for the educator who recognizes the value of science but isn't quite sure how to go about integrating science into an already full schedule. Every effort has been made to include scientific experiments and activities in this resource that use everyday materials, are easy to understand, easy to facilitate, and ignite a love for science.

An enthusiastic teacher introducing a scientific concept is much more effective in developing a love for science than a teacher with an extensive scientific background who does not understand how to build the connections that facilitate learning for young children. Teachers, who utilize everyday experiences and the numerous opportunities for incidental learning throughout the day, understand how to best maximize those learning connections and implement science education for young children.

The very nature of science lends itself to introducing students to inquiry-based learning. Inquiry-based learning is defined as the process of asking questions and trying to find answers for those questions. Implementing science activities throughout your curriculum will encourage your students' development of highly transferable critical thinking skills.

The experiments featured in this resource are aligned with the National Science Content Standards. This resource will provide you with developmentally appropriate experiments that focus on the following content areas: Physical Science, Life Science, Health, and Earth Science. Unifying concepts and processes, and science as inquiry are integrated into each experiment.

This book offers teachers of all backgrounds all they need to know to get started exploring science, hands-on.

How to Use this Book

Science Through the Year offers a wide variety of science activities and experiments. The book's format is easy-to-follow and teacher friendly. Every effort has been made to streamline the preparation time, recognizing the daily time constraints teachers face. Each unit of study is broken down in the following manner:

Materials

Each activity begins with a list of the necessary materials. For the most part, the materials can be found in a classroom, home, or home improvement or discount store.

Materials have been broken down into two parts. The first section, Demonstration Materials, lists items needed to introduce the activity, concept, and/or materials to students.

The second list, Student Materials, details what students will need to carry out their explorations individually or in small groups.

Getting Ready for the Activity

Specific instructions are provided as to what needs to be prepared prior to the activity. This information may include special materials that need to be found or purchased prior to the day of the activity, the amount of time needed for completion of the activity, and/or station breakdowns.

Recognizing the value of small group instruction, many of the experiments are divided into several "stations." Depending on the class size, group size will vary but generally the instructions are geared toward a group of 4–6 students. The advantages are many but, most notably, children learn best in small groups; and it allows the teacher to differentiate instruction and provide individualized attention during the activities.

Introduce the Activity

Introduction guidelines are provided, including a literacy connection for each experiment/activity. Taking the time to model/demonstrate the process for the experiment/activity provides the appropriate instruction for students. It also encourages students to develop listening skills, good work habits, and problem-solving skills.

It is suggested that teachers also present the new word cards at this time.

Procedure

Step-by-step instructions for students to complete each activity are provided. These steps are phrased simply, just as teachers would present activities to students. Copies of these steps can be made for parents and other room helpers if appropriate.

How to Use this Book *(cont.)*

Fun Science Questions and Facts

The information provided in this section answers commonly asked questions and provides enrichment information on the topic. In many instances, the information may seem more appropriate for older students, but teachers will benefit from this additional information and/or be able to extend activities when warranted.

Journal Pages

Every experiment/activity has a science journal page that reinforces a concept or skill that was introduced during the activity. The intent of the journaling emphasis is to provide a tangible way for teachers to give their students opportunities to make the connection between science and writing. Recording and/or documenting an observation is a valuable skill that will be strengthened through the activities in this book.

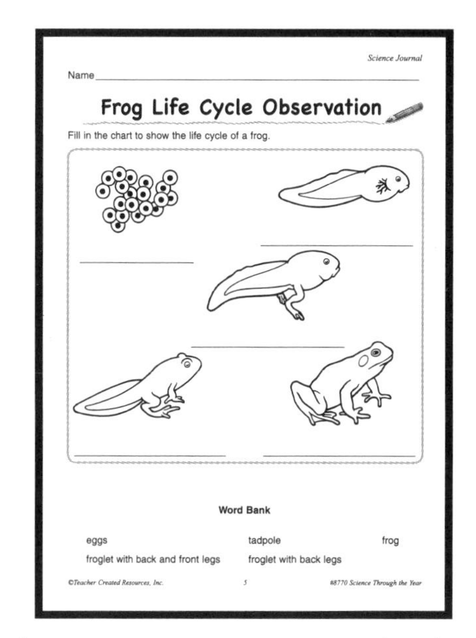
Science Journal

Name____________________

Frog Life Cycle Observation

Fill in the chart to show the life cycle of a frog.

Word Bank

eggs | tadpole | frog
froglet with back and front legs | froglet with back legs

©Teacher Created Resources, Inc. | 5 | #8770 Science Through the Year

For many teachers, the journaling pages will also serve as assessments for the various activities. Create a journal at the beginning of the year for each student to add to after each activity or create a Science Journal folder for each student to add individual pages to throughout the year. At the end of the year students can create covers or color the one provided on page 208 and assemble their journals.

Family Connections

Family Connections are included for the activities/experiments when it is considered beneficial and practical for families to be a part of the extension of the classroom activity. Sharing the day's activity, experiment, or mini book with parents is a great way to reinforce knowledge and practice new skills.

Note: Parent letters are provided when an item is being requested from home.

Word Cards and Station Cards

Vocabulary cards have been included for each activity and/or experiment. These should be copied onto card stock and laminated for durability. These cards will assist in reinforcing concepts of print and provide a connection between science and literacy. All students and especially English language learners will benefit greatly from the reinforcement of vocabulary that these cards will provide.

When possible, station cards have been included.

Helpful Hints and Resources

Helpful Hints

- ★ Shop at warehouse-type stores to purchase materials for experiments, such as vinegar, food coloring, baking soda, containers, etc.
- ★ Laminating charts will allow you to write on them with an overhead marker and reuse them.
- ★ Hairspray is a great fixative—spray on glitter, salt, rice, etc., and it works like a glue spray.
- ★ Permanent marker can be removed from laminated surfaces with hairspray or fingernail polish remover.
- ★ Create a chart by making an overhead of the desired material for the chart. Shine the overhead on the wall and trace it on a piece of chart paper.

Resources	Website
Creative Educational Surplus	*www.creativesurplus.com*
Discount School Supply	*www.discountschoolsupply.com*
Exploratorium	*www.exploratorium.com*
NASA	*www.nasa.gov/audience/foreducators/*
National Geographic	*www.nationalgeographic.com/education*
National Wildlife Federation	*www.nwf.org/education/*
Parent Science Handbook	*www.cascience.org/parenthandbook.pdf*
Science Made Simple	*www.sciencemadesimple.com*
Steve Spangler Science	*www.stevespanglerscience.com*
Science is Fun!	*scifun.chem.wisc.edu*
Educational Innovations, Inc.	*www.teachersource.com*
SK Science Kit and Boreal Laboratories	*www.sciencekit.com*
Shop 4 Tech	*www.shop4tech.com*
Carolina Biological Supply Company	*www2.carolina.com*
Water-Keep-environmentally safe super absorbent polymer crystals	*www.water-keep.com*
The Artistic Shop	*www.theartisticshop.com*
Soda Experiments	*www.eepybird.com*

Activity Breakdown

Experiment/Activity	Branch of Science	Page #	Family Connection	Mini Book
Details Are Important	Science Inquiry	11	x	
Rainbow Name	Physical	18		
Color Experiment	Physical	23	x	
Rainbow Crystals	Physical	29		
Rainbow Ice	Physical	36		
Sandcastles	Physical/Earth	42		
Crayon Resist Underwater Scene	Physical/Life	49		
Convection Currents Demonstration	Earth	56		
Apple Facts	Life/Health	61	x	x
Leaf Rubbings	Life	73	x	
Snow Crystals	Physical/Earth	80		
Ready, Set, React	Physical	85		
Static Electricity	Physical	90	x	
Fossils	Earth/Life/Physical	99		
Tooth Brushing Experiment	Life/Health	106	x	x
Shadow Pole Time	Earth	116		
Shadows	Earth	121		
Magnetism Experiment	Earth	128	x	
Pencil and Bag Experiment	Physical	134	x	
Air Tube Experiment	Earth	141	x	
Seed Sprouter	Life	148		x
Seedling Activities	Life	159		x
Seed Travel	Life	172	x	
Butterfly Symmetry	Life	180	x	
Frog Life Cycle	Life	190	x	
Soda Surprise	Physical	197		
Reduce, Reuse, Recycle, Redecorate	Earth	202	x	

Science Standards

Unifying Concepts and Processes

Definition: The processes of prediction, observation, recording, and evaluating are transferable into all curricular areas.

✔ **Overview**

Students will:

- be introduced to various systems, and the process of ordering and organizing data.
- observe various models and formulate explanations regarding the models.
- observe the changes in materials, both through measurement and observation.
- be introduced to the form and function of a wide variety of objects and materials.

Science As Inquiry

Definition: The scientific inquiry consists of asking meaningful questions and conducting careful investigations to find answers to those questions.

✔ **Overview**

Students will:

- develop their own questions.
- perform investigations.
- observe using their five senses.
- describe, compare, sort, and communicate their observations.

Physical Science

Definition: *Physics*: the interactions of matter and energy without chemical changes
Chemistry: the chemical interactions of atoms and molecules

✔ **Overview**

Students will:

- study the properties of objects and materials.
- observe the position and motion of objects.
- explore light, heat, electricity, and magnetism.

Based on National Science Education Standards

Science Standards *(cont.)*

Life Sciences

Definition: *Life science/biology*: the study of living things.

✔ **Overview**

Students will:

- expand their observational skills and vocabulary by learning to describe the characteristics of different animals and plants.
- be introduced to the life cycles of organisms.
- be introduced to organisms and various environments.

Health

Definition: *Health*: the study of health and health related issues.

✔ **Overview**

Students will:

- accept personal responsibility for lifelong health.
- understand ways in which personal health can be enhanced and maintained.
- understand behaviors that prevent disease.

Earth and Space Science

Definition: *Earth Science*: the study of the formation of and changes in our planet and the rest of the Universe.

✔ **Overview**

Students will:

- study the properties of earth materials.
- identify resources from Earth that are used in everyday life and understand that many resources can be conserved.
- be introduced to objects in the sky (moon, sun, stars).
- be introduced to changes in weather that occur from day to day and across seasons, affecting Earth and its inhabitants.

Based on National Science Education Standards

Alignment of Experiments and Activities to the National Science Education Standards

Page #	Activity/Experiment	National Science Education Standards						
		Unifying Concepts and Processes	Science as Inquiry	Physical Science		Life Sciences	Health	Earth and Space Science
				Physics	Chemistry			
11	Details are Important	X	X					
18	Rainbow Name	X	X	X				
23	Color Experiment	X	X	X				
29	Rainbow Crystals	X	X	X				
36	Rainbow Ice	X	X	X				
42	Sandcastles	X	X	X				X
49	Crayon Resist Underwater Scene	X	X	X		X		
56	Convection Currents	X	X					X
61	Apple Facts	X	X			X	X	
73	Leaf Rubbings	X	X			X		
80	Snow Crystals	X	X	X				X
85	Ready, Set, React	X	X		X			
90	Static Electricity	X	X	X				
99	Fossils	X	X	X		X		X
106	Tooth Brushing Experiment	X	X			X	X	
116	Shadow Pole Time	X	X					X
121	Shadows	X	X					X
128	Magnetism Experiment	X	X					X
134	Pencil and Bag Experiment	X	X	X				
141	Air Tube Experiment	X	X					X
148	Seed Sprouter	X	X			X		
159	Seedling Activites	X	X			X		
172	Seed Travel	X	X			X		
180	Butterfly Symmetry	X	X			X		
190	Frog Life Cycle	X	X			X		
197	Soda Surprise	X	X	X				
202	Reduce, Reuse, Recycle, Redecorate	X	X					X

Details Are Important

Demonstration Materials

- a rock
- a pencil
- a puzzle piece
- pencils, colored pencils, and crayons
- Science Journal—*Details are Important* (page 14)
- Word Cards—*Details are Important* (pages 16–17)

Student Materials

- 10 rocks of different shapes, sizes, and colors
- 10 pencils of different shapes, sizes, and colors
- 10 puzzle pieces of different shapes, sizes, and colors
- pencils, colored pencils, and crayons
- Science Journal—*Details are Important* (page 14)
- Family Connection—*Details are Important* (page 15)

Getting Ready for the Activity

1. Make copies of the Science Journal page. Give one copy to each student.
2. Make copies of the Family Connection page. Give one copy to each student.
3. Reproduce word cards on cardstock (or heavy paper), laminate, and display.
4. Prepare the following stations prior to student participation. Determine how and when students will rotate (plan on 10 minutes per station).

   Rock Observation Station: 10 different rocks, colored pencils, and crayons

   Pencil Observation Station: 10 different pencils, colored pencils, and crayons

   Puzzle Piece Observation Station: 10 different puzzle pieces, colored pencils, and crayons

Introduce the Activity

1. Read a book of your choice that reinforces the theme of observation. (**Suggestions:** *Take A Closer Look* by Tana Hoban; *Look! Look!* by Tana Hoban)
2. Introduce the word cards for the unit. Discuss the meaning of new words and concepts.
3. Explain that the class will divide up into three groups and participate in three separate observation experiments. Each student will complete the experiments using the materials present at each station.
4. Describe/demonstrate the procedure for each of the experiments before having students break off into the three groups.

Details Are Important *(cont.)*

Procedure

Station 1—Rock Observation

1. Choose a rock.
2. Observe the rock carefully.
3. Describe the rock to someone in your group. Use as many descriptive words as possible (e.g., rough, smooth, light, heavy, bright, dull, colorful, shiny, etc.).
4. Record your observation on the Science Journal page. Include as many details as possible.

Station 2—Pencil Observation

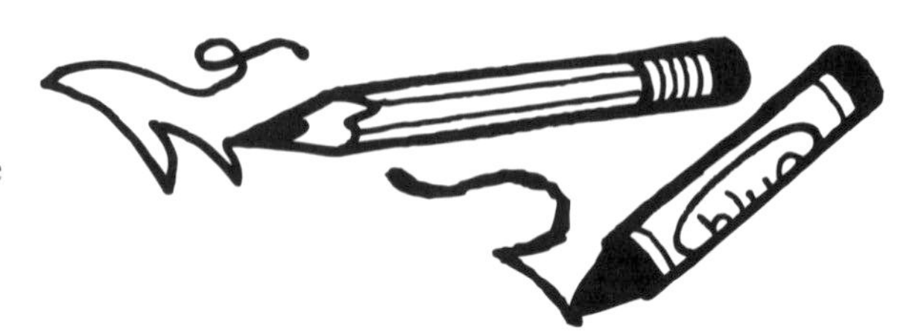

1. Choose a pencil.
2. Observe the pencil carefully.
3. Describe the pencil to someone in your group. Use as many descriptive words as possible (e.g., long, short, colored, smooth, light, heavy, shiny, etc.).
4. Record your observation on the Science Journal page. Include as many details as possible.

Station 3—Puzzle Piece Observation

1. Choose a puzzle piece.
2. Observe the puzzle piece carefully.
3. Describe the puzzle piece to someone in your group. Use as many descriptive words as possible (e.g., rough, smooth, light, heavy, bright, dull, colorful, corner piece, bumpy, etc.).
4. Record your observation on the Science Journal page. Include as many details as possible.

Follow Up

Return to each station and try to find the rock, pencil, or puzzle piece that you observed and recorded.

Family Connection

Ask students to take home the Family Connection page and complete the activity together as a family.

Fun Science Questions and Facts

What do the following words mean?

Observe: Giving careful attention (Looking closely at an object with attention to details.)

Describe: To give a verbal account of a person, scene, event, etc., (using words that convey the appearance of an object to someone else)

Record: An account made in permanent form (to draw or write about an observation with the intent of documenting what you observed)

Which object was the easiest to remember?

The object with the most distinctive features, bright colors, different shape, etc.

Why is it important to observe objects carefully?

If we can identify details, it is easier for us to remember them and describe them. It helps us to focus on the task and correctly evaluate the outcomes.

When have you needed to remember something accurately?

There is a need to remember addresses and phone numbers, backpacks, folders, our parents' cars, our classroom location, etc.

Is it easier to describe an object when you are looking at it?

Being able to see an object provides more sensory input and allows us to more accurately describe an object. The other senses of touching, hearing, tasting, and smelling are also important ways to gather information and help to describe an object accurately.

What types of jobs need people who can observe things closely?

People in many professions need to be skilled at observation. Doctors, artists, mechanics, clerks, accountants, etc.

Name ______________________________

Details are Important

Station 1—Rock Observation

This is a drawing of a ______________________________

Station 2—Pencil Observation

This is a drawing of a ______________________________

Station 3—Puzzle Piece Observation

This is a drawing of a ______________________________

Name ______________________________

Home School Connection

We are studying observation and documentation skills. Please help your child to complete the following observations in your home.

Spend some time talking with your child about these questions regarding observation and documentation.

- What is the best way to remember what something looks like?
- What objects did you observe at school today?
- Were you able to identify the object you observed and documented?
- What are some of the ways to describe objects?

Ask your child to look closely at your refrigerator for 15 seconds. Then ask your child go into another room and draw a picture of the refrigerator. Encourage him or her to include as many details as he or she can remember.

Have your child compare his or her drawing to your actual refrigerator. How many details did he or she include?

Ask your child to tell you what he or she would have changed if he or she had more time to observe the refrigerator before drawing it. ______________________

____

pencil

rock

puzzle

observe

document

record

describe

smooth

rough

shiny

dull

colorful

Rainbow Name

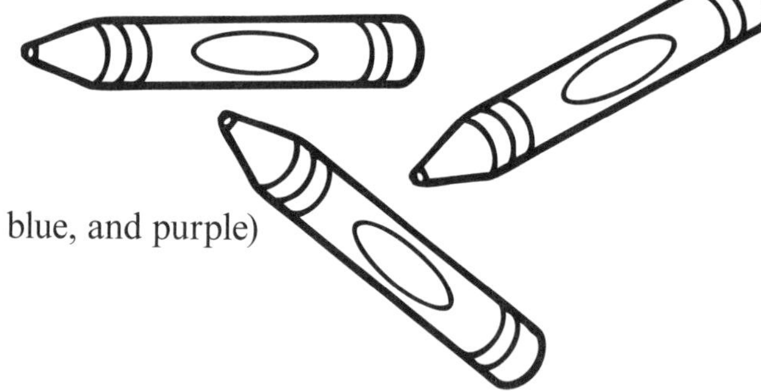

Demonstration Materials

- 12" x 18" white construction paper
- black permanent marker
- one set of crayons (red, orange, yellow, green, blue, and purple)
- Science Journal—*Rainbow Name* (page 21)
- Word Cards—*Rainbow Name* (page 22)

Student Materials

- 12" x 18" white construction paper (1 per student)
- set of crayons (red, orange, yellow, green, blue, and purple) (1 per student)
- Science Journal—*Rainbow Name* (page 21)

Getting Ready for the Activity

1. Make copies of the Science Journal page. Give one copy to each student.
2. Reproduce word cards on cardstock (or heavy paper), laminate, and display.
3. Print the teacher's name in large black letters across one piece of construction paper.
4. Print each student's name in large black letters across one piece of construction paper. Give one to each student.
5. Put a set of crayons on each desk.

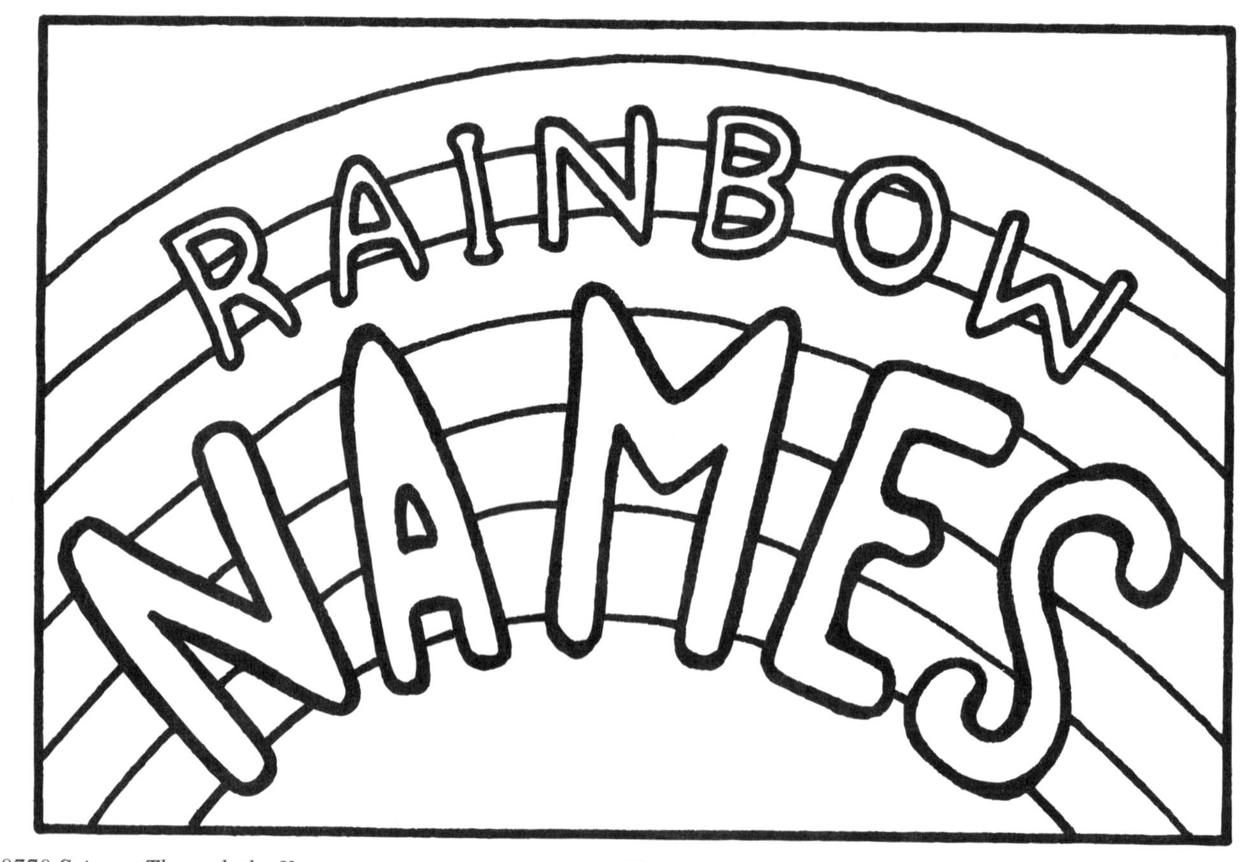

Rainbow Name *(cont.)*

Introduce the Activity

1. Read a book of your choice that reinforces the theme of colors. (**Suggestions:** *All the Colors of the Rainbow* by Allan Fowler; *Planting a Rainbow* by Lois Ehlert)
2. Review the colors of the rainbow (red, orange, yellow, green, blue, and purple).
3. Introduce the word cards for the unit. Discuss the meaning of new words and concepts.
4. Demonstrate this experiment to the entire class. Follow the steps outlined below.

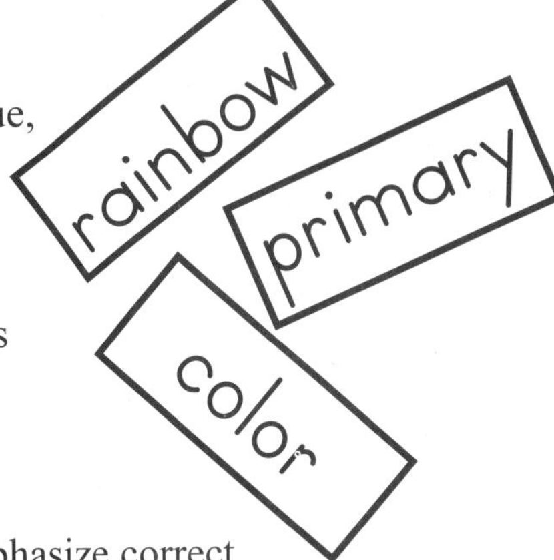

Procedure

1. Starting with the red crayon, trace the letters of your name. Emphasize correct printing (start at the top). Trace OVER the black line rather than around the letters.
2. Repeat the procedure using the remaining colors of the rainbow. Each letter should be traced with every color of the rainbow.
3. When finished, spell your name and then draw a picture of a rainbow on the Science Journal page. Draw the rainbow in the correct order from the top arc to the bottom arc (red, orange, yellow, green, blue, and purple).
4. Personalize the rainbow page by adding details to your picture.

Fun Science Questions and Facts

What are the colors of the rainbow?

Red, orange, yellow, green, blue, indigo, and violet. To simplify the concept, substitute purple for indigo and violet. The students will learn red, orange, yellow, green, blue, and purple as the rainbow colors.

Why are the colors always in the same order on a rainbow?

Sunlight may appear to be white, but it is really a mixture of colors. When you see a rainbow, the light is being refracted (or bent) at an angle that varies with each color. Violet is refracted the most, and it is always at the bottom. Red is refracted the least and is always at the top.

What makes a rainbow in the sky?

Sunlight is passing through a prism whenever you see a rainbow in the sky. The raindrops in the sky act as a prism and bend and reflect the light from the sun.

What other ways can we make a rainbow?

- This can be demonstrated in the classroom by taking a small prism and holding it at different angles while shining a light source through the prism. Try using an overhead projector and maneuvering the prism under the light source until you see rainbows on the ceiling in the room.
- Hanging a crystal prism in a window that receives direct sunlight will produce rainbows for your students.

Red	Orange	Yellow	Green	Blue	Purple

Name ____

Rainbow Name

Draw a picture of a rainbow. Add details to personalize your picture.

red

orange

yellow

green

blue

purple

Color Experiment

Demonstration Materials

- food coloring (red, blue, and yellow)
- water
- 4 clear plastic cups (9–12 oz)
- pipettes or eye droppers (several for each color of food coloring)
- crayons (red, orange, yellow, green, blue, and purple)
- Science Journal—*Color Experiment* (page 26)
- Word Cards—*Color Experiment* (page 28)

Student Materials

- 16 cups of colored water (4 red, 4 yellow, 4 blue, 4 regular water)
- pipettes or eye droppers (several for each color of food coloring)
- small bucket or container (1 per group)
- small pitcher of water (1 per group)
- crayons (red, orange, yellow, green, blue, purple)
- Science Journal—*Color Experiment* (page 26)
- Family Connection—*Color Experiment* (page 27)

Getting Ready for the Activity

1. Make copies of the Science Journal page. Give one copy to each student.
2. Make copies of the Family Connection page. Give one copy to each student.
3. Reproduce word cards on cardstock (or heavy paper), laminate, and display.
4. Offer your students pipettes and water prior to this activity, giving them time to practice using the pipettes.

Pipette Warm-up Activities

* Have each student practice squeezing the bulb at the end of the pipette. Place the pointed end into a container of water, loosen the grip on the bulb so that it inflates and the pipette fills up with water. Remove the filled pipette from the container and transfer the water into another container. Have the students predict and then count how many times the process needs to be repeated to fill up various sized containers.
* After they have mastered the pipette transfer, ask each student to count out a specific number of drops of water. (This is a great fine-motor activity to encourage the development of those skills that are necessary for printing.)

Color Experiment *(cont.)*

Getting Ready for the Activity (*cont.*)

5. Fill the clear cups 3/4 full with water. Add sufficient food coloring to produce vibrant primary colors. You will have 4 sets of the primary colors (red, blue, and yellow). Do not mix the colors to make secondary colors.
6. Place 1–2 pipettes in each cup of colored water. Place one set of the primary colors at each workstation. Include one clear cup 1/2 full of clear, plain water with each set of the primary colors. The colored water will be added to the plain water to create the secondary colors.
7. Place a small pitcher of water and a small bucket or container (1/2 full of water) at each workstation.
8. Place a set of crayons at each workstation.

Introduce the Activity

1. Read a book of your choice that reinforces the theme of color. (**Suggestions:** *Mouse Paint* by Ellen Stoll Walsh; *White Rabbit's Color Book* by Alan Baker)
2. Introduce the word cards for the unit. Discuss the meaning of new words and concepts.
3. Demonstrate this experiment to the entire class. Follow the steps outlined below.

Procedure

1. Use a pipette to add one color to the cup of clear, plain water. Observe what happens.
2. Record the first color on the Science Journal page, coloring the circle the appropriate color.
3. Choose a second primary color to add to the cup. Record the color on the Science Journal page. Make a prediction.
4. Use a pipette to add the second color to the first color in the cup. Observe the outcome (the secondary color) and record it on the Science Journal page. Share the outcome with the class (e.g., "Number one, red plus blue equals purple").
5. Repeat the procedure. Remember to predict, observe, record, and share the outcome before moving on. Continue to experiment until you complete the Science Journal page.

   Note: If necessary, pour out the mixed water into the buckets, rinse the cups, and use the pitchers to refill the cups.
6. Conclude the activity by having each pair "read" to each other their Science Journal page (e.g., "number one, red plus blue equals purple").

Family Connection

Ask students to take home the Family Connection page and complete the activity with their families.

Fun Science Questions and Facts

What are the primary colors?

Red, blue, and yellow

What are the secondary colors?

Orange, purple, and green

What are the complementary colors?

Purple/yellow, blue/orange, red/green. These two colors are in contrast to one another and appear brighter when together. If these pairs of colors are mixed, they dull each other.

What are warm colors? Cool colors? Neutral colors?

The warm colors (think of the sun) are red, orange, and yellow. The cool colors (think of the ocean) are green, blue, and purple. The neutral colors are black, white, and gray.

What type of color is brown?

It is called a *tertiary* color–the combination of all three primary colors.

What is it called when white is added to a color?

It is called a *tint*. When black is added, it is called a *shade*.

What are the colors of the rainbow?

Red, orange, yellow, green, blue, and purple (actually it's indigo and violet, but using purple simplifies the concept for young children).

Name ______________________________

Color Experiment

Fill in the following equations as you complete each color experiment. Use your crayons to color in each circle to indicate the color you are mixing.

Read each equation. For example: Number two, blue *plus* yellow *equals* green.

1.	○	+	○	=	○
2.	○	+	○	=	○
3.	○	+	○	=	○
4.	○	+	○	=	○
5.	○	+	○	=	○
6.	○	+	○	=	○
7.	○	+	○	=	○
8.	○	+	○	=	○

Name ____

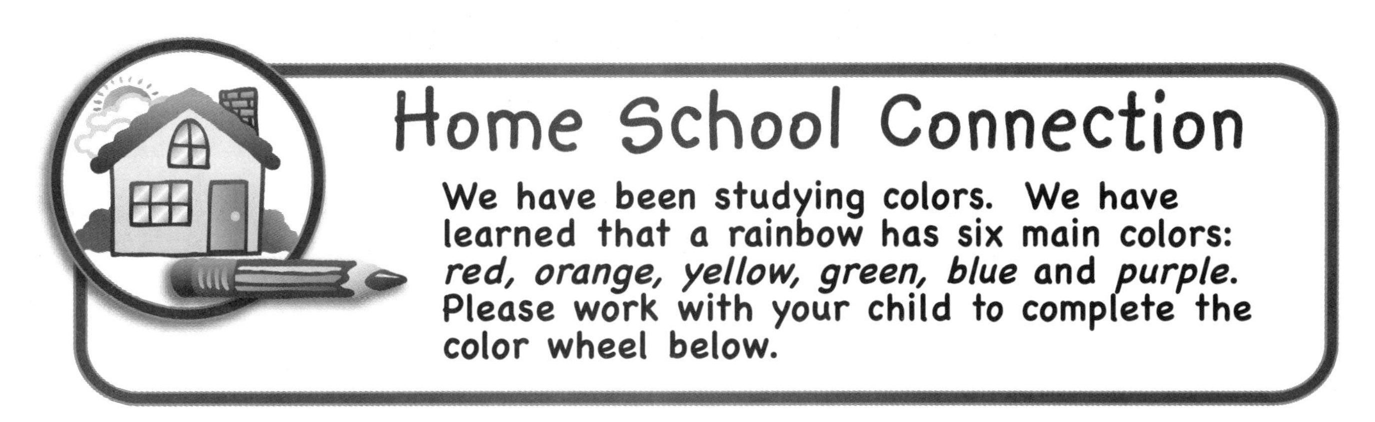

The following color wheel has already identified the sections that need to be colored in the primary colors. The sections in between will need to be colored in the secondary colors. You can identify the secondary colors because they are created when the colors on either side of the blank section are mixed. Refer to the word bank for the secondary color names.

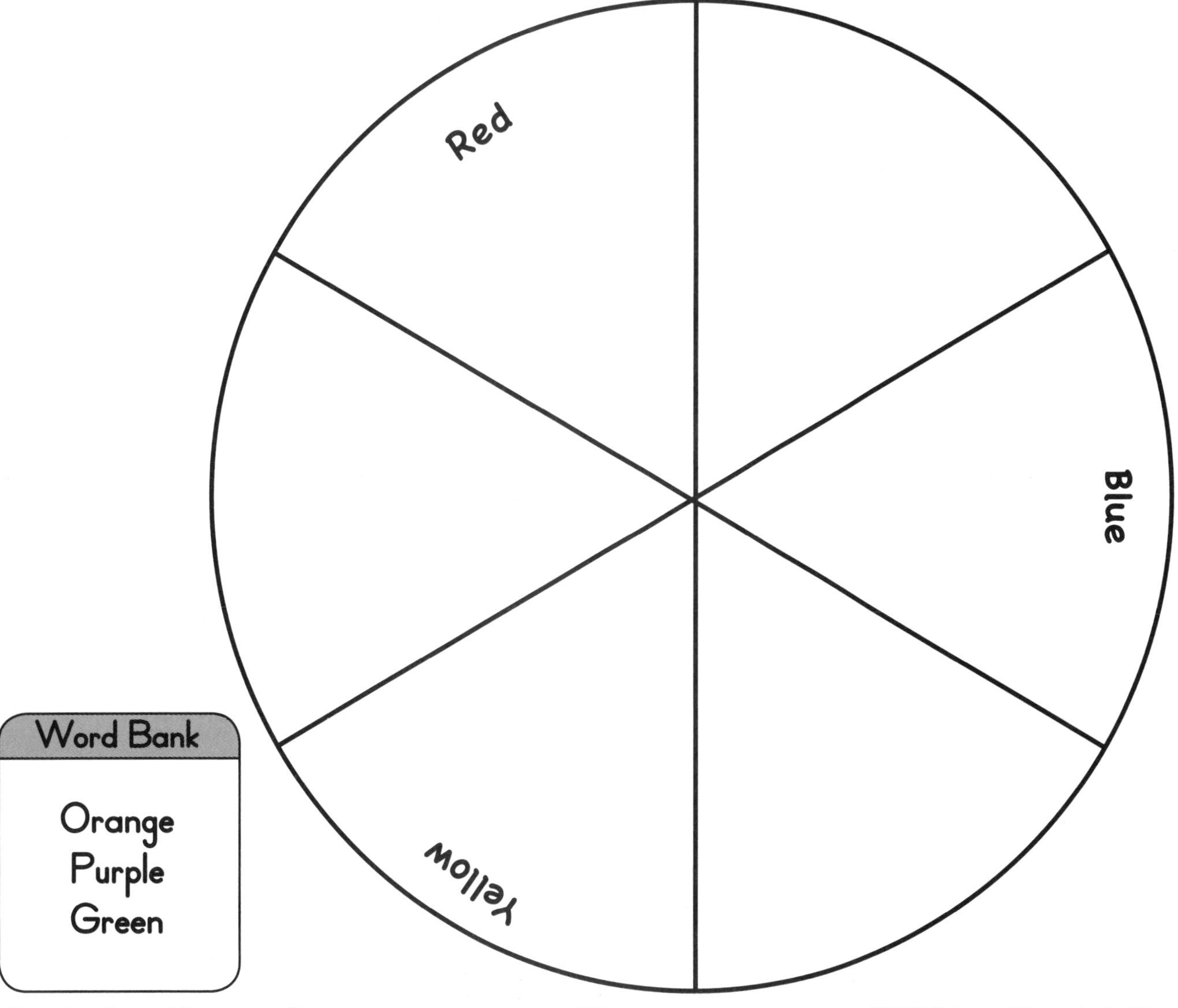

rainbow

primary

secondary

plus

equals

color

Rainbow Crystals

Demonstration Materials

- 12 oz. of dehydrated, water-absorbing crystals (You can find these crystals at plant nurseries, garden centers, and some educational companies. They are sold by various companies such as HydroSource® or SoilMoist®.) Use the crystals that DO NOT have any additives for plant growth.)
- food coloring (red, blue, and yellow)
- water
- tablespoon
- four, one-gallon resealable plastic bags
- clear containers (empty water bottles, graduated cylinders, clear cups, pre-form soda bottles) and one larger container to keep in the classroom (**Note:** Pre-form soda bottles can be purchased from *www.stevespanglerscience.com* or ordered from school supply companies.)
- crayons (red, orange, yellow, green, blue, and purple)
- Science Journal—*Rainbow Crystals Experiment* (page 33)
- Word Cards—*Rainbow Crystals Experiment* (pages 34-35)

Student Materials

- water-absorbing, hydrated crystals (red, blue, and yellow)
- clear container (1 per student)
- plastic wrap
- crayons (red, orange, yellow, green, blue, and purple) (1 set per student)
- Science Journal—*Rainbow Crystals Experiment* (page 33)

Getting Ready for the Activity

1. Make copies of the Science Journal page. Give one copy to each student.
2. Reproduce word cards on cardstock (or heavy paper), laminate, and display.

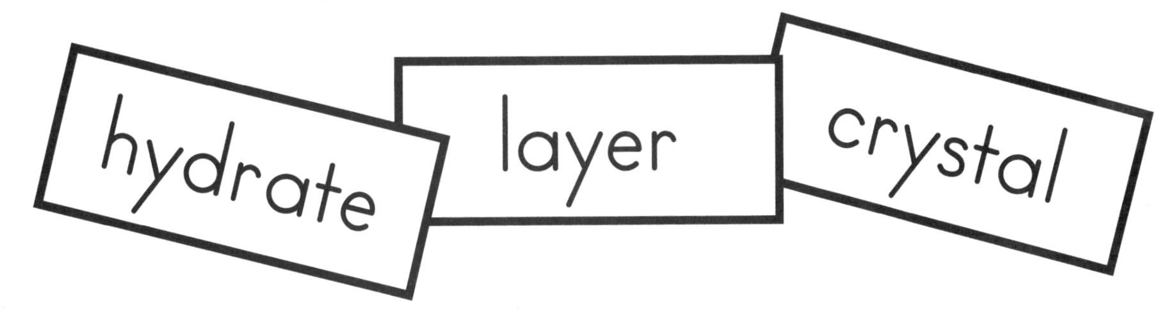

Rainbow Crystals *(cont.)*

Introduce the Activity

1. Read a book of your choice that reinforces the theme of color. (**Suggestions:** *White Rabbit's Color Book* by Alan Baker; *All The Colors of the Rainbow* by Allan Fowler)
2. Introduce the word cards for the unit. Discuss the meaning of new words and concepts.
3. Color and hydrate the crystals prior to the experiment. Follow the steps outlined below.

Part One–Coloring the Crystals

1. Pass around a small container of dehydrated crystals. Encourage the children to observe and describe the crystals.
2. Add two tablespoons of crystals to each gallon-size plastic bag.
3. Fill the plastic bag half full with water.
4. Add enough food coloring to create a vibrant primary color (red, blue and yellow) in each of the three bags. Leave the water in the fourth bag clear. Seal the tops of all the bags.
5. Set the bags of crystals inside a container to keep them upright.

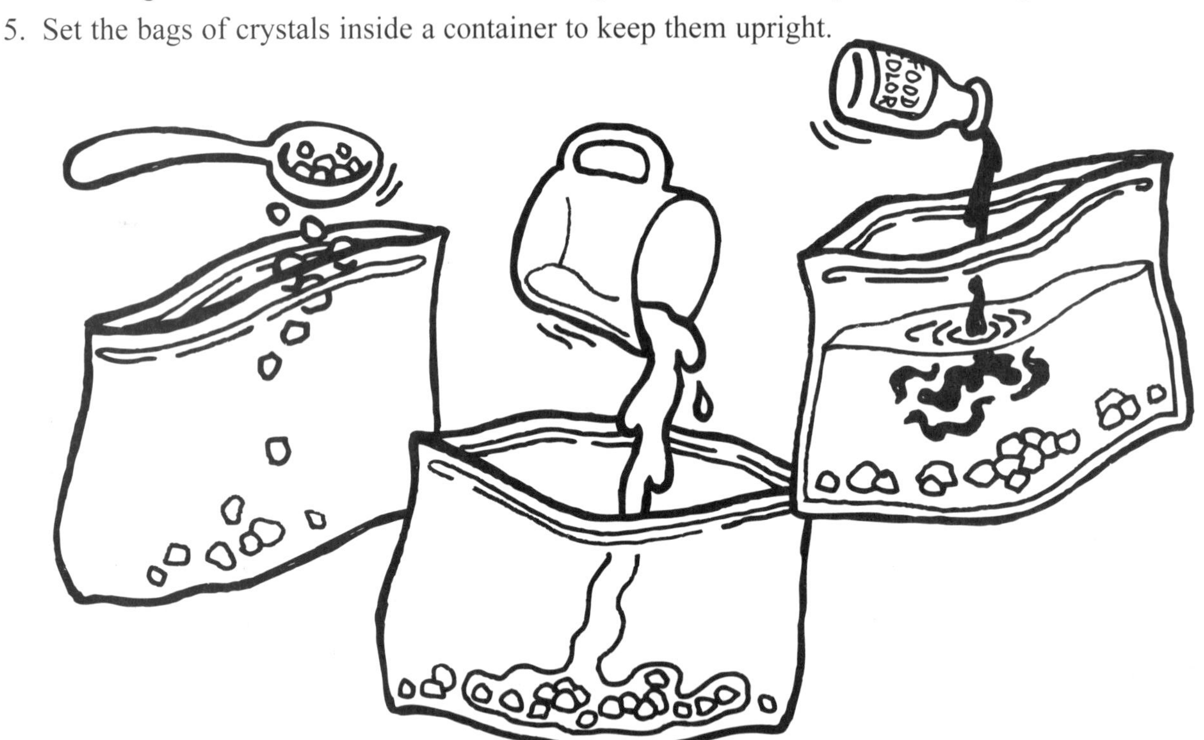

Part Two–Hydrating the Crystals

1. Check the crystals periodically. When they have absorbed all the water, you are ready to proceed. (It can take 1–2 hours for the crystals to become completely hydrated depending on conditions in the room.)
2. Place the containers and colored crystals at each workstation.

Rainbow Crystals *(cont.)*

Procedure

1. Pass around a cup of the hydrated colored crystals. Encourage students to observe and describe how the crystals have changed.
2. Review the colors of the rainbow. Is it possible to make a rainbow with the three primary colors: *red, yellow*, and *blue*? Demonstrate how to create a rainbow display using the large clear container.
3. Fill the bottom third of the clear container with the red crystals, the next third with yellow crystals, and the top third with blue crystals. Leave enough room to add a small layer of red crystals on the top to make purple. Seal the top of the container. If the container does not have a lid, use plastic wrap to seal it.
4. Have students create rainbow displays using the clear bottles. Refer to the classroom display as a model.
5. Have students observe closely for any changes and record observations on the Science Journal page.

Extension

Pour the clear crystals into a tub, creating a sensory activity for the children. Have them wash their hands before and after touching the crystals. (This will help to keep the crystals clean and last longer.) You can repeat this activity over a few days. Cover the crystals with plastic wrap or store them in an airtight container to keep them hydrated.

Fun Science Questions and Facts

What are these dehydrated crystals made out of? Are they dangerous?

They are a polymer, which is a long chain of molecules. Their official name is *cross-linked polyacrylamide copolymer gel*. They have been determined to be non-toxic and non-hazardous.

Who uses these crystals?

They are mostly used in the agriculture business by farmers and gardeners. Another form of this polymer is used in baby diapers due to its ability to absorb lots of liquid.

How long will they last?

The crystals will stay hydrated as long as they are kept in a sealed container. They will continue to "mix" colors and the rainbow will eventually be brownish. If you just mix two primary colors in the container and seal it, the crystals will remain the secondary color once they are totally mixed.

What would happen if I put them in my houseplants?

They can be mixed in your houseplants' soil to reduce the need to water. Be sure to hydrate them before mixing them into your houseplant soil, otherwise when you water your plant and the crystals expand they will push your plant out of the pot. For outside flower beds, you can just mix some into the soil around your plants.

What happens if they dry out? Can I reuse them?

Dehydrating the crystals is another activity for your class. Lay some out on a flat surface and observe what happens. After a couple of days they will be dehydrated back to their original size. At that time, you can rehydrate them by placing them in water. This process can be repeated over and over.

How long can I use them in a sensory table?

Consider them as a playdough-type product, the cleaner the hands that are exploring, the longer they will last. Sealing them up between uses will keep them hydrated.

What else can I do with the clear crystals?

- Using the clear crystals, you can also sprout seeds in a clear cup and observe the whole process.
- The clear crystals are a great way to allow children to see the roots of a plant. Take a small plant out of its soil, carefully rinse off its roots and place it into a clear cup filled with clear hydrated crystals. Add a little water until you can see the roots clearly. It will live in the crystals for a couple of weeks before running out of nutrients.

Name ____

Rainbow Crystals Experiment

Use crayons to record your observation of the rainbow crystals below.

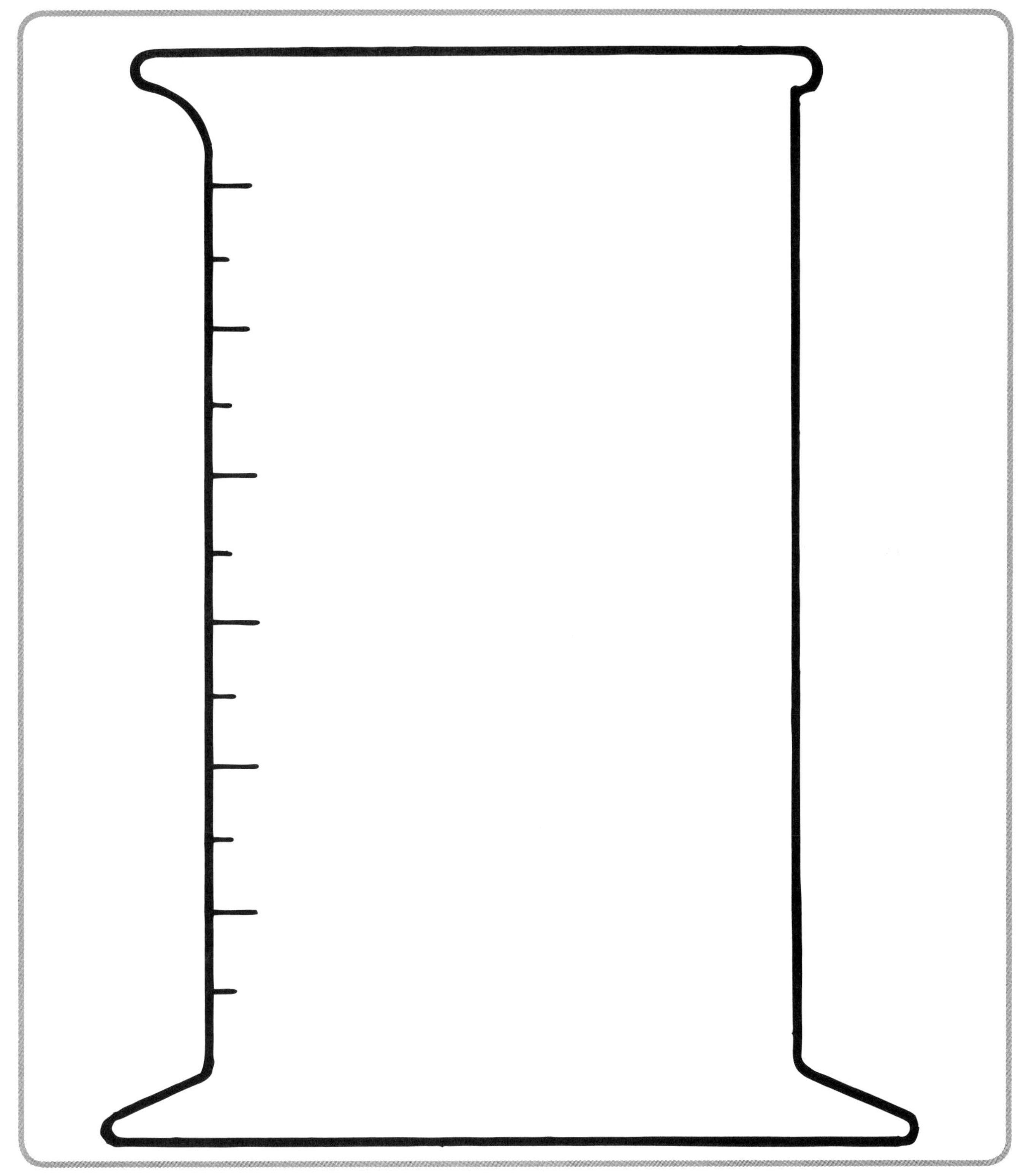

crystal

water

hydrate

dehydrate

color

layer

red

orange

yellow

green

blue

purple

Rainbow Ice

Demonstration Materials

- clear, shoebox-size plastic container
- food coloring (red, blue, and yellow)
- water
- 3 clear, plastic cups (9–12 oz)
- 3 pipettes or eye droppers
- various types of salt (table salt, Epsom salt, rock salt)
- block of ice (Freeze water inside of a container that fits inside the clear container for the experiment.)

  Note: Ice cubes will work, but they tend to melt quickly.

- 3 small bowls or containers
- 3 small plastic spoons
- Science Journal—*Rainbow Ice* (page 40)
- Word Cards—*Rainbow Ice* (page 41)

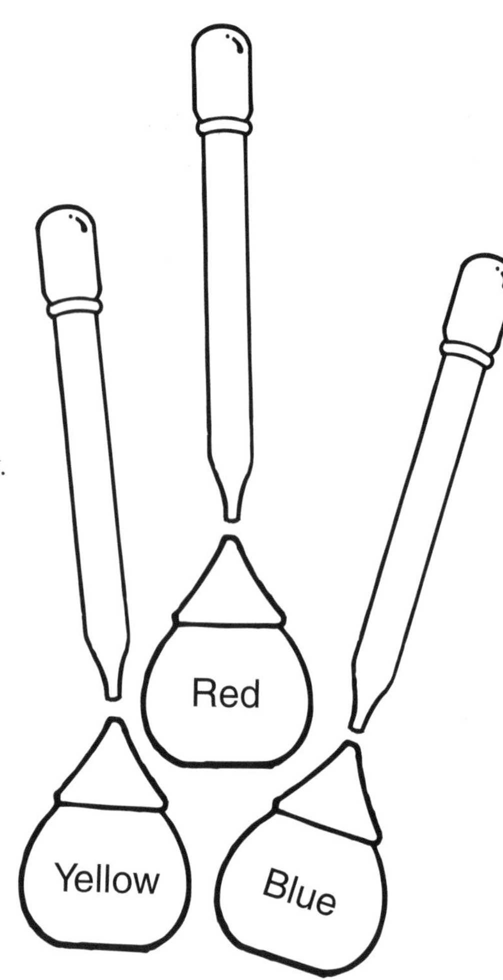

Student Materials

- clear, shoebox-size plastic containers (1 per group)
- colored water (red, yellow, and blue) in clear cups (1 set per group)
- pipettes or eye droppers (3 per group)
- various types of salt (table salt, Epsom salts, rock salt)
- blocks of ice (1 per group)
- small bowls or containers (3 per group)
- small plastic spoons (3 per group)
- Science Journal—*Rainbow Ice* (page 40)

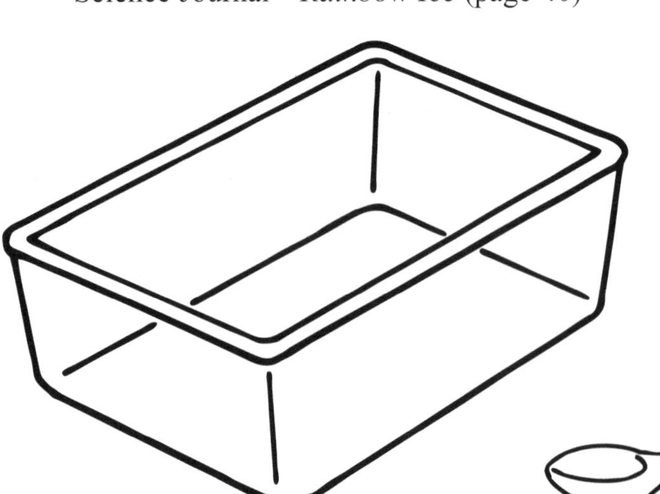

Rainbow Ice *(cont.)*

Getting Ready for the Activity

1. Make copies of the Science Journal page. Give one copy to each student.
2. Reproduce word cards on cardstock (or heavy paper), laminate, and display.
3. Pour salt into the small containers (one type of salt per container). Add one spoon to each container of salt. Place one set of containers of salt at each workstation.
4. Fill the clear, plastic cups 3/4 full with water. Add sufficient food coloring to produce vibrant primary colored water. Create four sets of the primary colored water (red, blue, and, yellow). Do NOT mix the colors to make secondary colors.
5. Place one pipette into each cup of colored water. Place one set of the colored water and pipettes at each workstation.
6. Remove the ice blocks from the freezer and place one into each of the clear, plastic containers. Place one at each workstation. (**Note:** The ice may be left out and observed throughout the day. Or, it may be rinsed off and put back in the freezer to be used again the next day.)
7. Divide the class into groups of 4–5 students.
8. Allow students to practice using the pipettes prior to the activity. (See page 23 for Pipette Warm-up Activities.)

Introduce the Activity

1. Read a book of your choice that reinforces the theme of color. (**Suggestions:** *Little Blue and Little Yellow* by Leo Lionni; *Color Dance* by Ann Jonas)
2. Introduce the word cards for the unit. Discuss the meaning of new words and concepts.
3. Demonstrate this experiment to the entire class. Follow the steps outlined on the following page.

Rainbow Ice *(cont.)*

Procedure

1. Use a pipette to transfer several drops of colored water onto the block of ice. Count the number of drops applied to the ice. Observe what happens.
2. Add a different color to the block of ice. Observe closely. What secondary color begins to appear?
3. Choose one type of salt. Pour a spoonful onto the ice. Observe the physical reaction that takes place. Listen carefully. What do you hear?
4. Continue to experiment with the colored water and salt.
5. Draw a picture of your observations on the Science Journal page.

Fun Science Questions and Facts

What is a physical reaction?

It is when two or more chemicals are mixed, and the by-product is a mixture of the two original chemicals. For example, if you mix salt (NaCl) and water (H_20), you will get saltwater, which is a mixture of the original chemicals, not a new chemical.

What is a chemical reaction?

It is when two or more chemicals are mixed, and the by-product is a different chemical than either of the original chemicals. For example, if you mix baking soda (sodium bicarbonate) and vinegar (acetic acid), a chemical reaction takes place and a different chemical (a carbon dioxide) is created.

What makes the Rainbow Ice experiment a physical reaction and not a chemical reaction?

The salt (NaCl) is added to the water (H_20), and it causes the ice to melt and form salt water. To be a chemical reaction, there would need to be created a by-product of the reaction that is different from the original chemicals.

Why does the ice make cracking noises?

When ice thaws and refreezes, it makes cracking noises as it expands and contracts.

Have you ever seen someone use salt to melt ice?

Salt is commonly used in parts of the country where it snows to keep the ice from forming on the roads and sidewalks. When salt is added to ice, some of the salt actually dissolves by pulling water away from the ice crystals. The melted ice-salt mixture is colder than 0 degrees Celsius or 32 degrees Fahrenheit. The salt lowers the freezing point of water.

Why not just let the students use all six colors of the rainbow?

Producing the secondary colors reinforces the concept of primary and secondary colors.

What type of color is brown?

It is called a *tertiary* color—the combination of all three primary colors.

What are the colors of the rainbow?

Red, orange, yellow, green, blue, and purple (Actually, it's indigo and violet, but using purple makes sense for young children.)

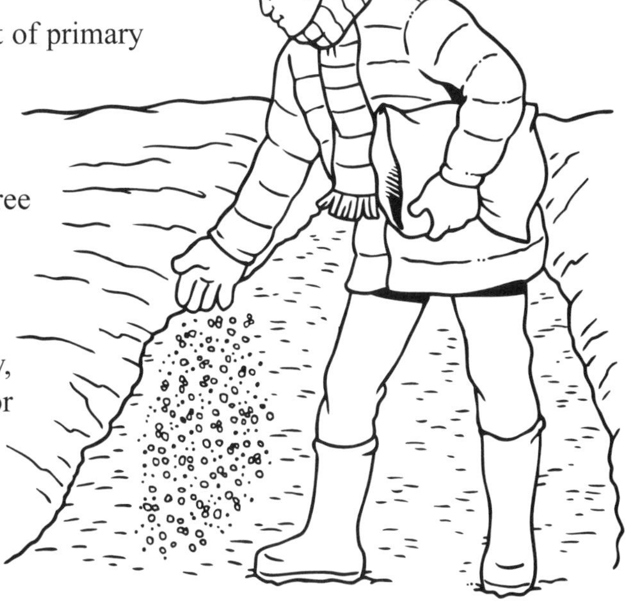

Name ____

Rainbow Ice

Draw a picture of the rainbow ice.

ice

melt

salt

mix

freeze

water

Sandcastles

Demonstration Materials

- white glue (16–32oz.)
- water (approximately one gallon)
- large tub of damp sand (1/2 full)
- large tub of soapy water (to wash hands)
- half gallon container (must hold water)
- variety of plastic cups (8 oz. or smaller)
- variety of containers (no larger than 1 cup)
- sand molds, funnels, scoops (e.g., 2 oz. scoop from baby formula)
- heavy-duty paper plate or piece of cardboard
- toothpicks
- self-sticking mailing labels (to make flags)
- clay tools (to add details to sandcastles)
- crayons, pencils, markers, watercolors, paint
- all-purpose craft glue
- small confetti fish
- small seashells
- Science Journal—*Sandcastles* (page 47)
- Word Cards—*Sandcastles* (page 48)

Student Materials

- damp sand in a large tub (2 cups per student)
- white glue (16–32oz.)
- large tub of damp sand (1/2 full)
- large tub of soapy water
- variety of plastic cups (8 oz. or smaller)
- variety of containers (no larger than 1 cup)
- sand molds, funnels, scoops (e.g., 2 oz. scoop from baby formula)
- heavy-duty paper plate or piece of cardboard (1 per student)
- toothpicks
- self-sticking mailing labels (1 per student)
- clay tools (to add details to sandcastles)
- crayons, pencils, markers, watercolors, paint
- all-purpose craft glue
- small confetti fish
- small seashells
- Science Journal—*Sandcastles* (page 47) (1 per student)

Sandcastles *(cont.)*

Getting Ready for the Activity

1. Make copies of the Science Journal page. Give one copy to each student.
2. Reproduce word cards on cardstock (or heavy paper), laminate, and display.
3. Prepare a Sandcastle Workstation. (This is messy, but worth it.) Choose a workspace that is easy to clean. It should have a bare floor and a trashcan.
4. Prepare a container of glue/water mixture: Fill the 1/2-gallon container with 48 oz. of water. It should be 3/4 full. Add 16 oz. of white glue and mix well. Be prepared to repeat this procedure as needed.
5. Place the tub of sand in the work area. Keep a separate container of sand nearby to use if the sand/glue mixture becomes too wet.
6. Place the tub of soapy water in the work area.
7. Place the plastic cups, containers, and other sand molds in the work area.
8. Fold the mailing labels over the top of the toothpicks to create flags. Have student decorate their flags. These will later be placed on top of their sand castle.
9. Give each student a plate or cardboard base. Ask them to write their name along the edge of the base.
10. Designate an area where the sandcastles can dry safely for a few days.

Introduce the Activity

1. Read a book of your choice that reinforces the theme of oceans or sandcastles. (**Suggestions:** *The Magic School Bus on the Ocean Floor* by Joanna Cole; *Hiding in a Coral Reef* by Patricia Whitehouse; *Sun Sand Sea Sail* by Nicki Weiss)
2. Introduce the word cards for the unit. Discuss the meaning of new words and concepts.
3. Demonstrate this experiment to the entire class. Follow the steps outlined on the next page.

Sandcastles *(cont.)*

Procedure

1. Add the glue/water mixture to the tub of sand. Mix until the sand is moist, but not dripping wet.
2. Test the mixture by filling one of the containers, packing the sand inside, and turning the container over onto a cardboard base.
3. Gently tap the top or squeeze the sides of the container as you slowly lift the container straight up. The sand form should hold its shape. If it is too dry and crumbles, add more glue/water mixture. If it is too wet, it won't hold its shape and will become a blob. Add more sand. Adjust the sand mixture, until it holds its shape when molded.
4. Practice creating different sand forms with the different containers. If you do not like what you make, dump it back into the tub and start again. Consider combining shapes to create more elaborate castles.

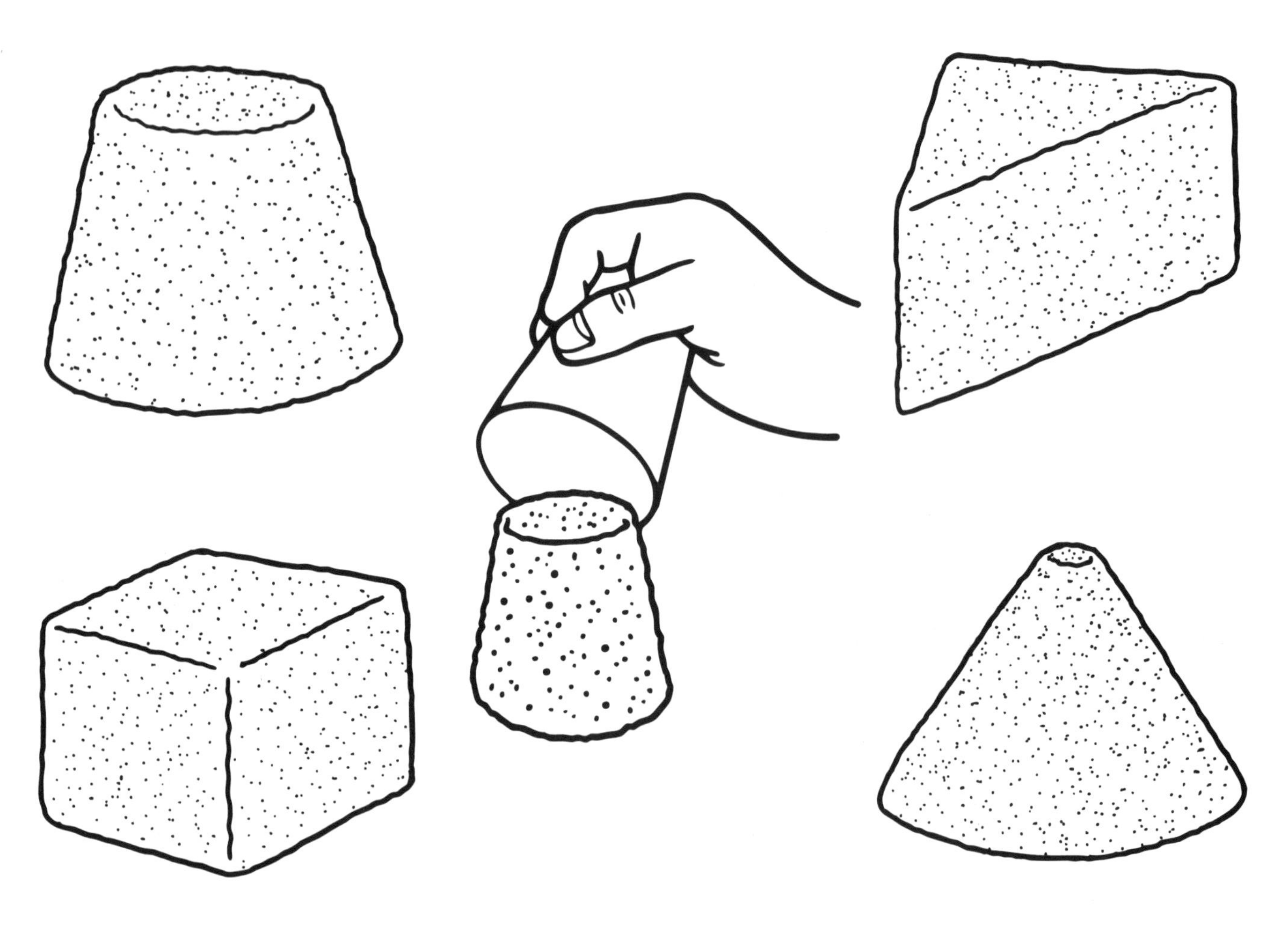

Sandcastles *(cont.)*

Procedure *(cont.)*

5. Use the toothpicks to make portholes, designs, etc. on your sandcastles. Stick your decorated flag in the top of it.
6. Transport the sandcastles to the drying area. Be extra careful! If bumped, the castles may crumble.
7. Clean up is made easier if all the sandy materials are put in the tub of soapy water and allowed to soak. Use a wet cloth to wipe off the tables. Cover any extra sand mixture with plastic wrap or put it into a sealed plastic bag. The glue/water mixture can also be stored in a sealed container for later use.
8. Check on the sandcastles each day until they are solid and hard to the touch. Decorations can be glued to the sandcastle once it is dry. Detail the base with watercolors, paint, markers, small confetti fish, and seashells.
9. Draw a picture of your sandcastle on the Science Journal page.
10. These sandcastles are great for doorstops, outdoor decorations, or gifts.

Fun Science Questions and Facts

What is sand made out of?

It is made of bits of stone, shell, and coral. Use a magnifying glass to examine the particles of sand.

What is going to happen to your sandcastle? Why?

The sand will become hard as the sand particles are stuck together by the glue mixture.

Why did some containers work better than others? Which worked the best?

Containers with smooth sides and at least one small hole in the bottom worked best. The sides allowed the sand to slide out and the hole on the bottom didn't allow the container to form a vacuum, so the sand came out easily.

Will I be able to change my sandcastle tomorrow?

Once the sand particles are glued together and dry, it becomes one large sand rock. It will be very difficult to make any structural changes.

What would happen if I put my hardened sandcastle in a tub of water?

As the glue dissolves in the water, the sand particles will be released and you will end up with the materials you started with: sand and the glue/water mixture. The process of the sand becoming solidified illustrates how a physical reaction works. The materials created by the reaction can be returned to their original state. No new materials were created.

Name____

Sandcastles

After carefully observing your sandcastle, draw a picture of what it looks like.

glue

water

sand

particles

solidify

reaction

Crayon Resist Underwater Scene

Demonstration Materials

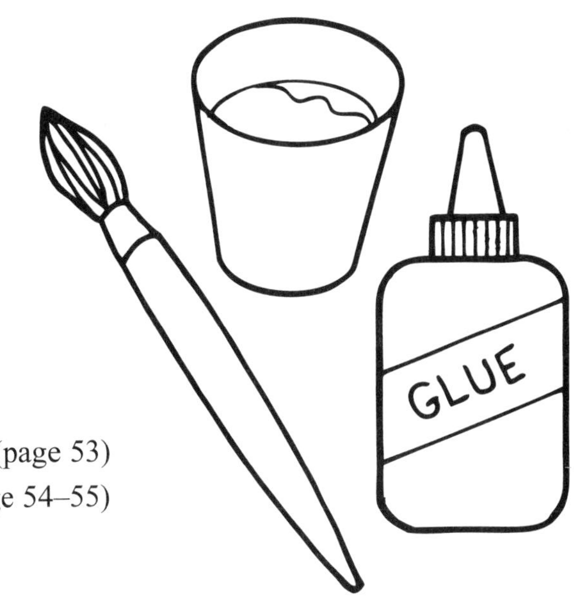

- white copy paper
- crayons
- water
- blue tempera paint
- 1” paint brush
- newspaper or other paper to cover table surface
- white glue or glue stick
- a marker
- various colors of construction paper (9" x 12")
- Science Journal—*Crayon Resist Underwater Scene* (page 53)
- Word Cards—*Crayon Resist Underwater Scene* (page 54–55)

Student Materials

- white copy paper (1 per student)
- Science Journal—*Ocean Life* (page 53)
- crayons
- water
- blue tempera paint
- 1” paint brushes (1 per group)
- newspaper or other paper to cover table surface
- white glue or glue sticks
- fine-point markers (1 per group)
- various colors of construction paper (9" x 12") (1 per student)

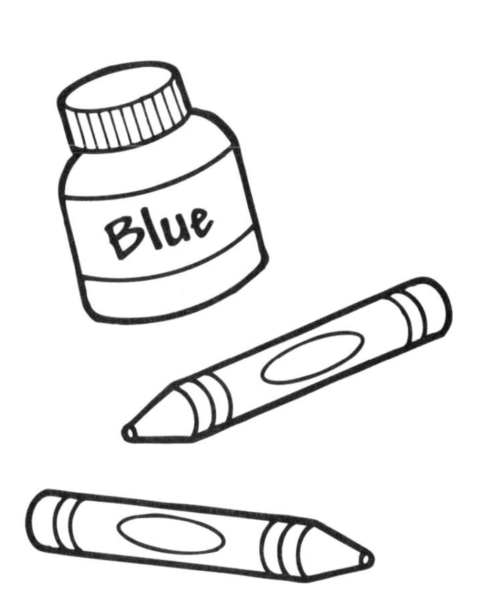

Crayon Resist Underwater Scene *(cont.)*

Getting Ready for the Activity

1. Give each student a large piece of white copy paper.
2. Reproduce word cards on cardstock (or heavy paper), laminate, and display.
3. Create the "wash" for this activity by mixing 1 ounce of blue paint to 1 cup of water.
4. Cover the painting area with newspaper or newsprint.

Introduce the Activity

1. Read a book of your choice that reinforces the theme of underwater ocean life.
   (**Suggestions:** *Big Al* by Andrew Clements; *Swimmy* by Leo Lionni; *One Small Fish* by Joanne Ryder)
2. Introduce the word cards for the unit. Discuss the meaning of new words and concepts.
3. Demonstrate this experiment to the entire class. Follow the steps outlined on the following page.

Crayon Resist Underwater Scene (cont.)

Procedure

1. Print your name on the back of the white copy paper.
2. Use crayons to draw an ocean scene, pressing down hard with the crayons.
3. Paint over the entire picture with the "wash," the watered-down blue tempera paint.
4. Turn the picture upside down onto the newspaper. Rub lightly on the back to remove excess paint.
5. Set the painting face up on a flat surface to dry.
6. Glue the dry painting to a piece of construction paper. This will keep your picture flat, provide a border, and make it easy to display.
7. Add a creative title (e.g., Friendly Fish) to the border.

Extension: Have students complete the *Ocean Life* journal page.

Fun Science Questions and Facts

Why doesn't the paint cover the entire paper?

If you have colored on the paper with a crayon, wax has transferred from the crayon to the paper. Wax repels the water by plugging the pores of the paper, and the wash does not color the part of the paper with wax.

Why are some of my fish blue and others are not?

The fish that were not completely colored with crayon will not repel the wash, and the paper will be colored blue.

What will happen if we use markers?

Markers do not leave wax on the paper and will not repel the wash. If you used markers, your whole page would be the color of the wash.

What else can you think of that is made out of wax?

Candles are made of wax.

Could we complete this experiment using a candle instead of a crayon? Why or why not?

It would be possible although the candle colors will not transfer the way crayon colors show up on paper.

What makes this a science activity?

Paper is made from wood, which has porous fibers. These fibers or capillaries act like a sponge and absorb water. If the capillaries are blocked, the water will not be absorbed into the paper. The wax from the crayons in this experiment is blocking the capillaries in the paper and not allowing them to absorb the wash. The parts of the paper that have not been colored with crayons have no wax blocking the capillaries, and therefore will absorb the blue wash and turn blue.

Name ____

Ocean Life

Draw a picture of your favorite ocean animal.

ocean

animal

resist

water

crayon

background

paper

cover

wax

repel

absorb

pores

Convection Currents

Demonstration Materials

- 4 plastic water containers with tapered necks
- red and blue food coloring
- hot and cold tap water
- 2 index cards
- Science Journal—*Convection Currents* (page 59)
- Word Cards—*Convection Currents* (page 60)

Student Materials

- crayons (red, orange, yellow, green, blue, and purple)
- Science Journal—*Convection Currents* (page 59)

Getting Ready for the Activity

1. Make copies of the Science Journal page. Give one copy to each student.
2. Reproduce word cards on cardstock (or heavy paper), laminate, and display.
3. Fill two containers with cold water and add blue food coloring.
4. Fill the other two containers with hot water and add red food coloring.
5. Show the colored water to the students. Explain that the blue water is cold, and the red water is hot.

Introduce the Activity

1. Read a book of your choice that reinforces the theme of currents or color. (**Suggestions:** *The Magic School Bus in the Arctic: A Book About Heat* by Joanna Cole; *Heat and Cold* by Peter Lafferty)
2. Introduce the word cards for the unit. Discuss the meaning of new words and concepts.
3. Demonstrate this experiment to the entire class. Follow the steps outlined on the following page.

Convection Currents *(cont.)*

Procedure

1. Place an index card on the top of one bottle of red water. Carefully hold the card in place and quickly turn the bottle over. Set it down directly over the bottle of blue water. The trick is to hold the card firmly against the mouth of the bottle as you turn it over, and then align the bottles once the card is in between the mouths of both bottles. Align the necks of the bottles and pull the index card out, allowing the red water to mix with the blue water.

2. Observe what happens. Record your observations on the Science Journal page.

3. Predict what will happen when the blue water is placed on top of the red water. Put the index card on the top of the second bottle of blue water. Hold the card in place, turn the bottle over, and set it down directly over the top of the bottle of red water. Align the bottles and pull the index card out allowing the water to mix.

4. Observe what happens. After five minutes, record your observation on the Science Journal page.

Fun Science Questions and Facts

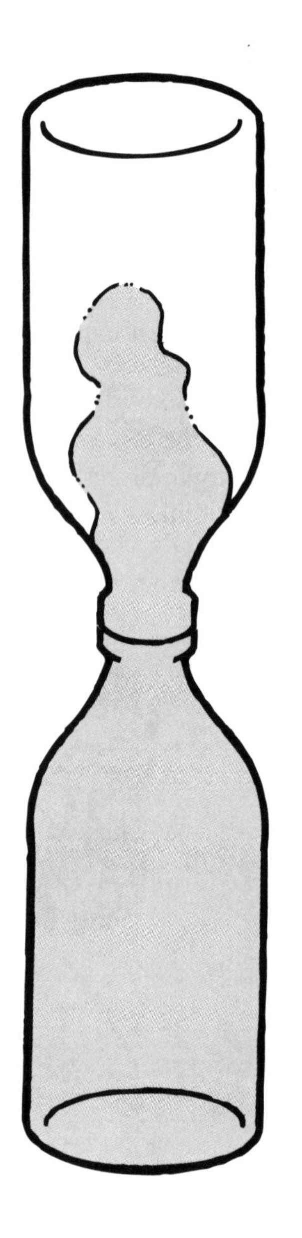

Why does the red water go to the top?

The density of a fluid varies with temperature. Warmer fluids are less dense and will rise, while colder fluids are more dense and will sink.

How hot does the water need to be for this experiment to work?

It does not need to be boiling, just hot to the touch.

What will happen after 30 minutes? Why?

Both sets of bottles will be purple. As the red water cools off, it will become heavier and sink, thus mixing with the blue water to make purple.

How else can we see convection currents?

If you add rheoscopic fluid to colored water, it allows you to see the currents in the water. Rheoscopic fluid is used in cosmetics (lotion, shampoo) and is also sold by some educational supply companies. One part Glycol Stearate soap to four parts of water will also allow you to see the convection currents in water. Try doing the experiment using baby lotion.

On a hot day, would you rather be upstairs or downstairs? Explain.

Since the hot air travels upward and the cooler air downward, it should be cooler downstairs.

In an ice chest, to keep the contents coldest, where should the ice go? On the bottom or top?

Since cold air sinks and travels downward, it makes sense to put the ice on top of the contents in the ice chest and allow it to cool off what's underneath it.

In a swimming pool, where is the warmest water?

Heat rises, so the warmer water will be closest to the surface of the water.

Name ____

Convection Currents

Draw a picture of what happens when the *red* water is mixed with the *blue* water.

Red

Blue

Draw a picture of what happens when the *blue* water is mixed with the *red* water.

Blue

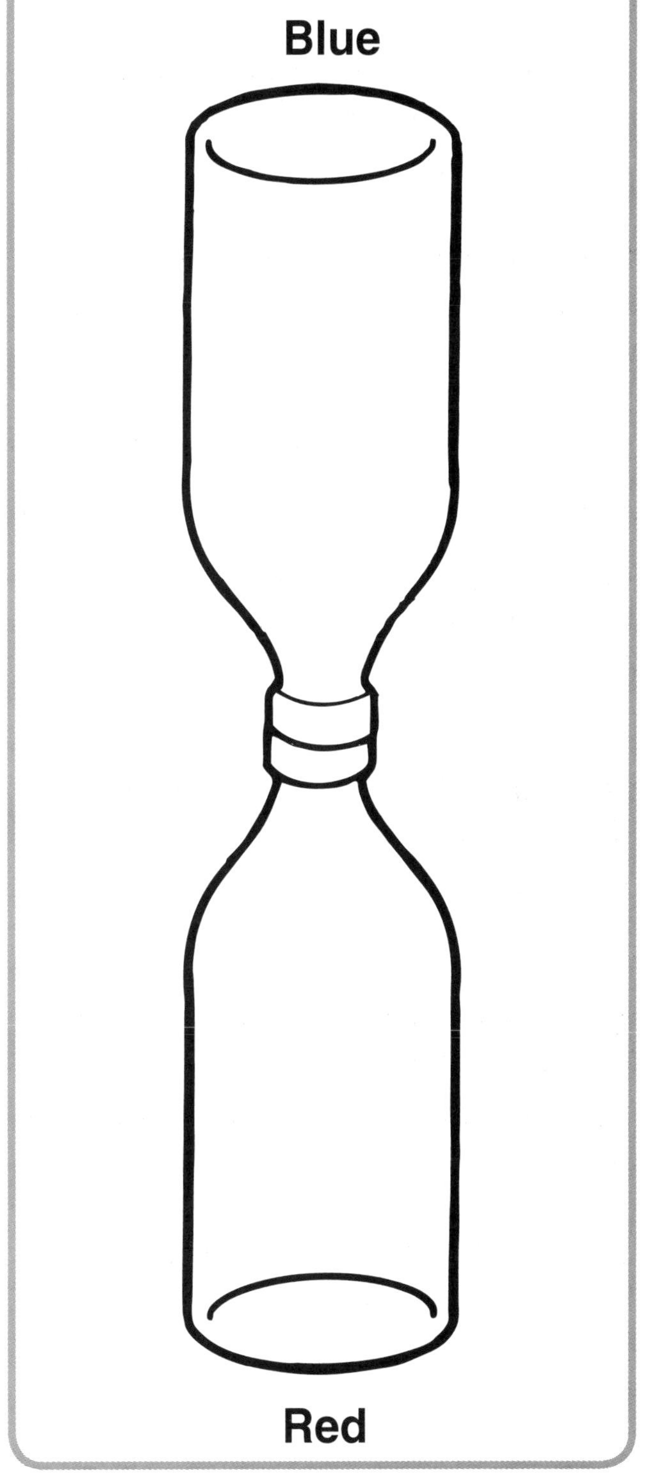

Red

hot

cold

current

water

rise

sink

Apple Facts

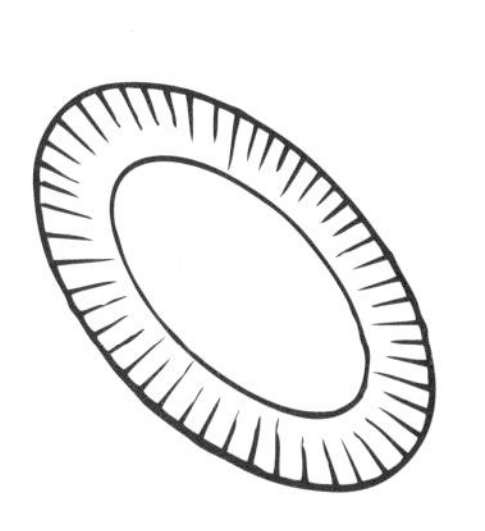

Demonstration Materials

- an apple
- a small kitchen scale
- measuring tape
- cutting board and knife
- crayons, colored pencils, and pencils
- paper plate and napkin
- toothpick
- tub of water
- Mini Book—*Apple Facts* (pages 65–67)
- Word Cards—*Apple Facts* (page 70–71)
- Station Cards—*Apple Facts* (page 72)

Student Materials

- apples in a variety of colors and sizes (1 per student)
- small kitchen scales
- measuring tape
- cutting board and knife (to be used by an adult)
- crayons, colored pencils, and pencils
- paper plates and napkins (1 each per student)
- toothpicks
- tub of water
- Mini Book—*Apple Facts* (page 65–67)
- Family Connection—*Apple Facts* (page 68)
- Parent Letter—*Apple Facts* (page 69)

Getting Ready for the Activity

1. Make copies of the Mini Book. Assemble each book prior to the activity. Give one copy to each student.
2. Make copies of the Family Connection page. Give one copy to each student.
3. Make copies of the Parent Letter. Send it home with students prior to the activity.
4. Reproduce word cards on cardstock (or heavy paper), laminate, and display.
5. Prepare the following stations prior to student participation. Determine how and when students will rotate (plan on 10 minutes per station).

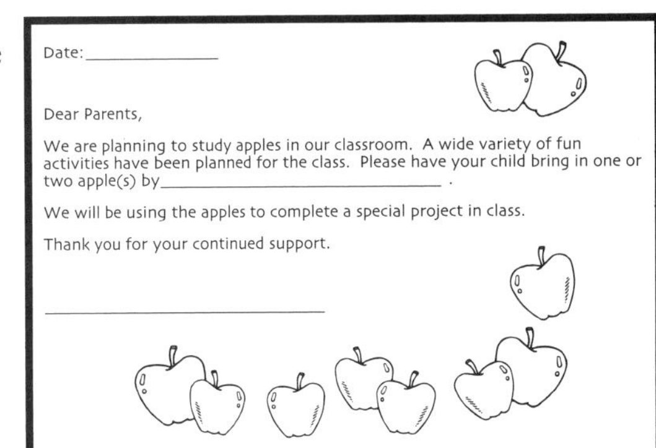

Date:____________

Dear Parents,

We are planning to study apples in our classroom. A wide variety of fun activities have been planned for the class. Please have your child bring in one or two apple(s) by____________________________ .

We will be using the apples to complete a special project in class.

Thank you for your continued support.

____

Apple Facts *(cont.)*

Getting Ready for the Activity *(cont.)*

Station 1—Observation

- colored pencils, crayons, and pencils
- Observation Station Card

Station 2—Measuring and Weighing

- measuring tape
- kitchen scales
- colored pencils, crayons, and pencils
- Measuring and Weighing Station Card

Station 3—Counting Seeds and Tasting

- cutting board
- knife
- paper plates
- napkins
- toothpicks
- tub of water
- pencils, crayons, and colored pencils
- Counting Seeds and Tasting Station Card

Safety Note: *An adult needs to be at the Counting Seeds and Tasting station to cut the apples for the students.*

Introduce the Activity

1. Read a book of your choice that reinforces the theme of apples. (**Suggestions:** *Apples* by Gail Gibbons; *How Do Apples Grow?* by Betsy Maestro)
2. Introduce the word cards for the unit. Discuss the meaning of new words and concepts.
3. Explain that the class will divide up into *two* groups and participate in *three* separate observation experiments. Students can begin at Station 1 or 2. All students will need to end at Station 3. Each student will complete the experiments using the materials present at each station.
4. Describe the procedure for each of the experiments before having students break off into the two groups. Each student will complete Stations 1 and 2 before moving to Station 3. Students will need to observe, measure, and weigh their apples in Station 1 and 2 before cutting their apples in Station 3.
5. On the way to the first station, give each student an apple and a Mini Book. Explain to students that they will need to take both of these items to all three stations.

Apple Facts *(cont.)*

Procedure

Station 1—Observation

1. Observe your apple and draw a picture of it on the cover of the Mini Book.
2. Complete page 1 of the book.

Station 2–Measuring and Weighing

1. Measure the circumference (how far around the outside) of the apple.
2. Record your measurement on page 2.
3. Use the kitchen scales to weigh the apple.
4. Record the mass of the apple on page 3.

Station 3–Counting Seeds and Tasting

1. Wash the apple in the tub of water. Wash your hands, too.
2. Have an adult cut the apple in half. (Cut it horizontally to display the seed "star" in the core of the apple.)
3. Use toothpicks to carefully remove the seeds from the core of the apple.
4. Record the number of seeds found in the apple on page 4 of the Mini Book. Draw a picture of the seeds.
5. After finding all the seeds, taste the apple.
6. Complete the sentence on page 5.
7. Share one fact about your apple with the others in your group.

Family Connection

Ask students to take home the Family Connection page and complete the activity with their families.

Fun Science Questions and Facts

What is the most popular apple in the United States?

The Red Delicious apple, which originated in Iowa in 1881, is the most popular apple.

How many different types of apples are there?

In the world, there are 7,500 different varieties. In the U.S. there are 2,500 varieties of apples grown.

Where do apples grow?

Apples are grown all over the world. In fact, apple trees are grown in more places than any other fruit tree.

Who is Johnny Appleseed? Did he really plant apple trees?

John Chapman was a real man who lived in the early 1800s. He planted apple trees in Ohio, Pennsylvania, and Indiana. His nickname became Johnny Appleseed, because he visited with settlers and shared his apple seeds with them.

How long does it take for an apple to grow?

An apple tree needs to be 5–8 years old before it will produce any apples. A mature apple tree will blossom in the springtime, and its apples will be ready to be harvested in the fall.

Apple Facts

By: ______________________

My apple is ______________________ .

My apple is ____ inches/centimeters around.

My apple weighs _________ grams/ounces. 3

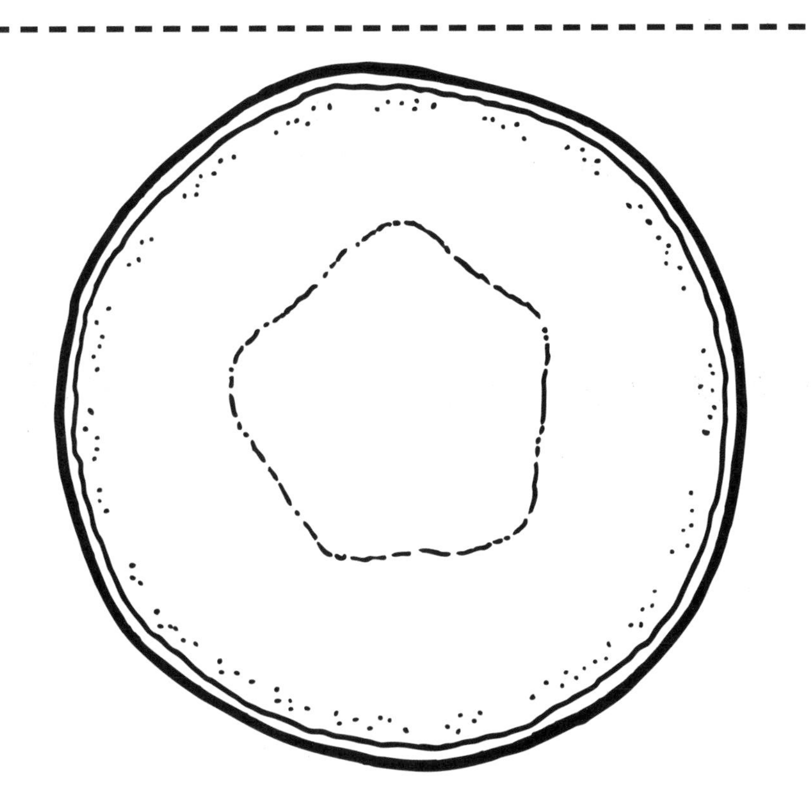

My apple has ______________ seeds.

My apple tastes ______________________.

Name ____

Home School Connection

We are studying apples. Your child is completing an Apple Facts Mini Book. Please have him or her read it to you and discuss what the class discovered as they explored their apples in class.

Ask your child to name as many foods as he or she can think of that have apples as an ingredient. Then, have your child choose his or her favorite apple food and draw a picture of it below.

My favorite apple food is ____ .

Did you know?

Apples are the most widely grown fruit in the world. There are 7,500 different varieties of apples grown in the world.

Date: ________________

Dear Parents,

We are planning to study apples in our classroom. A wide variety of fun activities have been planned for the class. Please have your child bring in two apples by ___________________________________ .

We will be using the apples to complete a special project in class.

Thank you for your continued support.

____

Date: ________________

Dear Parents,

We are planning to study apples in our classroom. A wide variety of fun activities have been planned for the class. Please have your child bring in two apples by ___________________________________ .

We will be using the apples to complete a special project in class.

Thank you for your continued support.

____

mass

weigh

measure

apple

sweet

sour

seed

core

pollinate

tree

blossom

ripe

Observation
Measuring & Weighing
Counting Seeds & Tasting

Leaf Rubbing

Demonstration Materials

- white paper
- a variety of fresh and dry leaves
- peeled crayons
- magnifying glass
- Science Journal—*Leaf Rubbing* (page 76)
- Word Cards—*Leaf Rubbing* (page 79)

Student Materials

- white paper (1 per student)
- a variety of fresh and dry leaves
- peeled crayons
- magnifying glasses (1 per group)
- Science Journal—*Leaf Rubbing* (page 76)
- Parent Letter—*Leaf Rubbing* (page 77)
- Family Connection—*Leaf Rubbing* (page 78)

Getting Ready for the Activity

1. Make copies of the Science Journal page. Give one copy to each student.
2. Make copies of the Family Connection page. Give one copy to each student.
3. Make copies of the Parent Letter. Send it home with students prior to the activity.
4. Go on a nature walk to collect a variety of leaves from around your campus.
5. Reproduce word cards on cardstock (or heavy paper), laminate, and display.
6. Peel the paper off of the crayons.

Leaf Rubbing *(cont.)*

Introduce the Activity

1. Read a book of your choice that reinforces the theme of leaves. (**Suggestions:** *Why Do Leaves Change Color?* by Betsy Maestro; *Red Leaf, Yellow Leaf* by Lois Ehlert; *Autumn Leaves* by Ken Robbins)
2. Introduce the word cards for the unit. Discuss the meaning of new words and concepts.
3. Demonstrate this experiment to the entire class. Follow the steps outlined below.

Procedure

1. Print your name on a piece of white paper.
2. Choose a couple of leaves and observe them with the magnifying glass.
3. Place one leaf with the vein-side up on the table. Position the paper over the leaf.
4. Hold a crayon horizontally. Carefully rub the crayon over the paper directly above the leaf.
5. Repeat with other leaves.
6. Choose a different leaf and create another leaf rubbing on the Science Journal page.

Family Connection

Ask students to take home the Family Connection page and complete the activity with their families.

Fun Science Questions and Facts

Why do leaves change color in the fall?

Some trees go dormant for the colder winter months. In preparation for the winter, the leaves will start to separate from the tree. As they separate, they will get less water. Without water, leaves cannot make new chlorophyll, which gives them their green color. The green color fades, and the fall colors appear before the leaves fall off the tree.

Which leaves made the best rubbings? Why?

Leaves that are freshly picked will be able to withstand the pressure of the rubbing without cracking. This is due to their water content.

What types of trees did the leaves come from?

Research to find out the types of trees that are in your neighborhood. Use a tree identification resource book to classify the leaves.

What are the lines on the leaf rubbings?

The lines are the veins. Leaves have veins which distribute nutrients to all the cells in the leaf.

What other objects could you use to make rubbings?

Coins and textured, flat objects make good rubbings. Try making rubbings of roof shingles, bricks, water meter covers on the ground, etc.

Name ____

Leaf Rubbing

Choose a leaf and create a leaf rubbing in the frame below.

Date:_______________

Dear Parents,

We are planning to study leaves in our classroom. Please have your child collect 5–10 leaves to bring to class by ____________________ .

Thank you for your continued support.

____

Date:_______________

Dear Parents,

We are planning to study leaves in our classroom. Please have your child collect 5–10 leaves to bring to class by ____________________ .

Thank you for your continued support.

____

Date:_______________

Dear Parents,

We are planning to study leaves in our classroom. Please have your child collect 5–10 leaves to bring to class by ____________________ .

Thank you for your continued support.

____

Name____

Home School Connection

We are studying leaves. We created leaf rubbings this week at school. Please accompany your child on a nature walk and gather a few leaves to use to make rubbings.

Ask your child to demonstrate how to make a leaf rubbing. Complete several leaf rubbings below. Ask your child to explain the function of the veins in the leaves.

leaf

vein

stem

rough

color

rubbing

Snow Crystals

Demonstration Materials

- dark blue or black construction paper (12" x 18")
- white crayon
- a plastic container (margarine tub)
- Epsom salts
- water
- paint brushes (2 different sizes)
- magnifying glass
- Science Journal—*Snow Crystals* (page 83)
- Word Cards—*Snow Crystals* (page 84)

Student Materials

- dark blue or black construction paper (12" x 18") (1 piece per student)
- white crayons
- plastic containers (1 margarine tub per group)
- Epsom salts
- water
- paint brushes (variety of sizes) (2–3 per group)
- magnifying glasses (2–3 per group)
- Science Journal—*Snow Crystals* (page 83)

Getting Ready for the Activity

1. Make copies of the Science Journal page. Give one copy to each student.
2. Reproduce word cards on cardstock (or heavy paper), laminate, and display.
3. Prepare the salt solution in small containers. Fill a container 1/2 full of Epsom salts. Add water and stir until the solution is saturated. There should be some undissolved salt in the bottom of the container. Also, the solution should be thin enough to be brushed onto paper.
4. Place the paper, white crayons, paint brushes, and magnifying glasses at each workstation.

Science Journal

Name ____________________

Snow Crystals

Using a magnifying glass, look closely at your snow painting. Draw a picture of one of the crystal structures on your paper.

©Teacher Created Resources, Inc. 80 #8770 Science Through the Year

Snow Crystals *(cont.)*

Introduce the Activity

1. Read a book of your choice that reinforces the theme of snow.
   (**Suggestions:** *The Big Snow* by Berta Hader; *The Snowy Day* by Ezra Jack Keats; *The Snowflake: A Watercycle Story* by Neil Waldman)
2. Introduce the word cards for the unit. Discuss the meaning of new words and concepts.
3. Demonstrate this experiment to the entire class. Follow the steps outlined below.

Procedure

1. Use the white crayon to print your name on the piece of dark construction paper.
2. Dip the paintbrush into the salt solution and "paint" a picture on your paper.
3. Use a magnifying glass to observe the crystals that form on the paper. (Depending on the saturation of the solution, the crystals will continue to form over time as the paper dries.)
4. When the painting is finished and the crystals have been observed, complete the Science Journal page.

Fun Science Questions and Facts

What makes the crystals appear on the paper?

As the solution dries, the water evaporates and the salt remains. Then, the salt crystals begin to show on the paper.

Are all the crystals the same?

Each crystal is unique, just like snowflakes (no two snowflakes are the same).

What is salt made out of?

Salt (sodium chloride) is made up of two elements: sodium and chlorine (NaCl).

How many different types of salt are there?

The types are table salt, sea salt, Epsom salt, and rock salt. They are all made of salt crystals, but the texture and size of the crystals are different.

Are there other salt experiments?

Saturate a solution of table salt in a small clear container. Using a string, tie a paper clip to a pencil and hang the clip into the solution. As the solution evaporates, salt crystals will form on the string and paper clip. This will happen slowly over a period of days, depending on weather conditions.

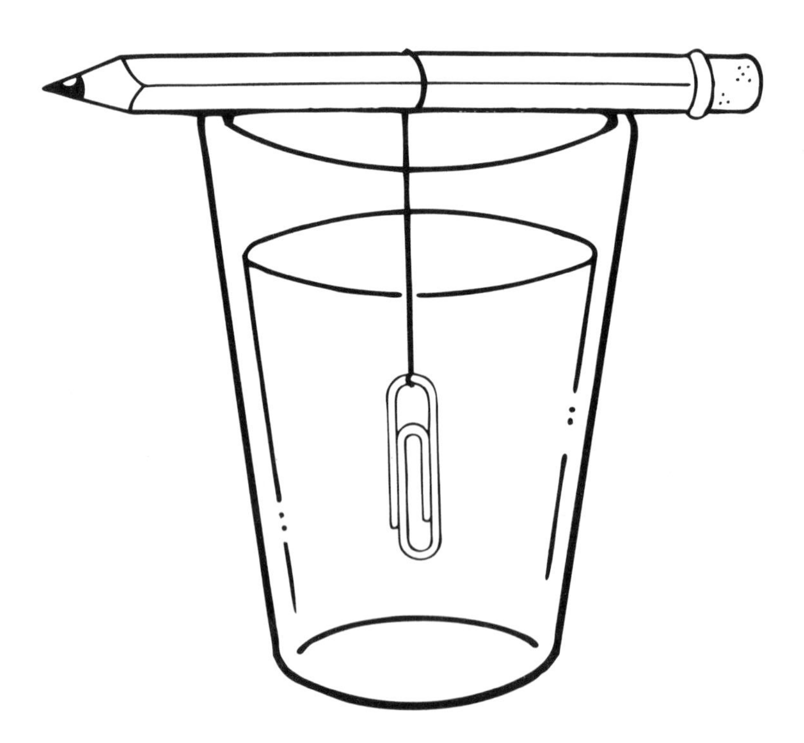

Name ____

Snow Crystals

Using a magnifying glass, look closely at your snow painting. Draw a picture of one of the crystal structures on your paper.

snow

white

crystal

water

salt

solution

Ready, Set, React

Demonstration Materials

- one empty plastic bottle (16–20 oz.)
- baking soda (2 tablespoons)
- 1/4 cup of white vinegar
- 1-2 balloons (8"–10")
- measuring spoon (1 tablespoon)
- measuring cups
- index card
- Science Journal—*Ready, Set, React* (page 88)
- Word Cards—*Ready, Set, React* (page 89)

Student Materials

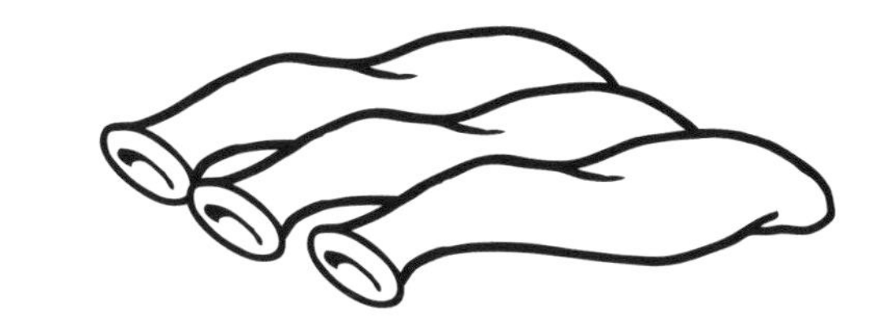

- 16–20 oz. plastic bottles (1 per student)
- baking soda (2 T. per student)
- index cards
- white vinegar (1/4 cup per student)
- balloons (1–2 per student)
- measuring spoons (1 T.) (2 per group)
- measuring cups (1 per group)
- Science Journal—*Ready, Set, React* (page 88)

Getting Ready for the Activity

1. Make copies of the Science Journal page. Give one copy to each student.
2. Reproduce word cards on cardstock (or heavy paper), laminate, and display.
3. Collect empty bottles and rinse them out. (Ask students to bring them in prior to the experiment.)
4. Tape an index card to create a cone-shaped funnel. Use the funnel to fill each balloon with 2 tablespoons of baking soda. Balloons should be filled for students prior to the activity.
5. Place vinegar and measuring cups at each workstation.

Introduce the Activity

1. Read a book of your choice that reinforces the theme of chemical reactions. (**Suggestion:** *Volcano: Jump Into Science* by Ellen Prager)
2. Introduce the word cards for the unit. Discuss the meaning of new words and concepts.
3. Demonstrate this experiment to the entire class. Follow the steps on the following page.

Ready, Set, React *(cont.)*

Procedure

1. Pour 1/4 cup of vinegar into your empty bottle.
2. Stretch the neck of the balloon onto the neck of the bottle. Be very careful not to spill the baking soda. Be sure the balloon is covering the neck of the bottle. (**Note:** Have one student hold the bottle while another student stretches the balloon over the neck of the bottle.)

3. Hold the balloon tightly onto the neck of the bottle. Lift the bottom of the filled balloon and gently pour the baking soda into the bottle of vinegar.
4. Observe closely as a chemical reaction takes place inside the bottle. The balloon should inflate with the gas that is being produced by the reaction.
5. Draw a picture of the reaction on the Science Journal page.

Note: This experiment may be repeated by changing the variables. Try using different kinds of bottles, different amounts of baking soda and vinegar, and different sizes of balloons.

Fun Science Questions and Facts

Why did the balloon blow up?

When the baking soda (sodium bicarbonate–$NaHCO_3$) makes contact with the vinegar (acetic acid), it creates a chemical reaction that produces carbonic acid. The unstable, carbonic acid almost immediately breaks down into carbon dioxide (CO_2) and water. The carbon dioxide is a gas, and it rises in the bottle, blowing up the balloon.

What type of gas is produced?

Carbon dioxide is produced when the two chemicals mix. It is the gas that humans and animals exhale every time they breathe.

How can I get my balloon to blow up really BIG?

To increase the quantity of gas, you would need to change the variables in the experiment (quantities of vinegar and baking soda, the bottle size, and the balloon size).

Are there other substances I could use to get my balloon to blow up?

Some experiments have been conducted to compare the results of mixing vinegar with baking powder instead of baking soda. It also will produce carbon dioxide, but much less than the baking soda and vinegar reaction. You can also mix Alka Seltzer® and water (same amount as vinegar).

Name ____

Ready, Set, React

Draw a picture of what you observed during this experiment.

balloon

baking soda

vinegar

gas

liquid

solid

Static Electricity

Demonstration Materials

- 9"–12" balloons
- 18" piece of string
- Styrofoam pieces (beads from beanbags, packing peanuts, etc.)
- a continuous stream of water, preferably from a faucet
- Science Journal—*Static Electricity* (page 94)
- Word Cards—*Static Electricity* (pages 96–97)
- Station Cards—*Static Electricity* (pages 98)

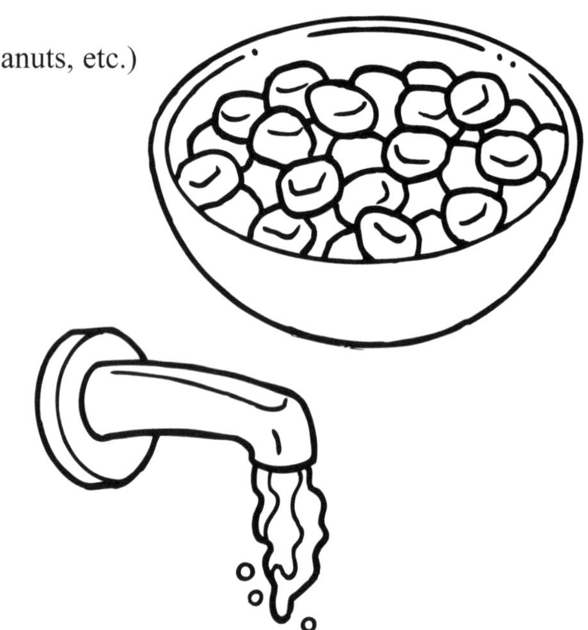

Student Materials

- 9"–12" balloon (1 per students)
- 18" piece of string (1 per student)
- Styrofoam pieces (10–15 per student)
- a continuous stream of water, preferably from a faucet
- Science Journal—*Static Electricity* (page 94)
- Family Connection—*Static Electricity* (page 95)

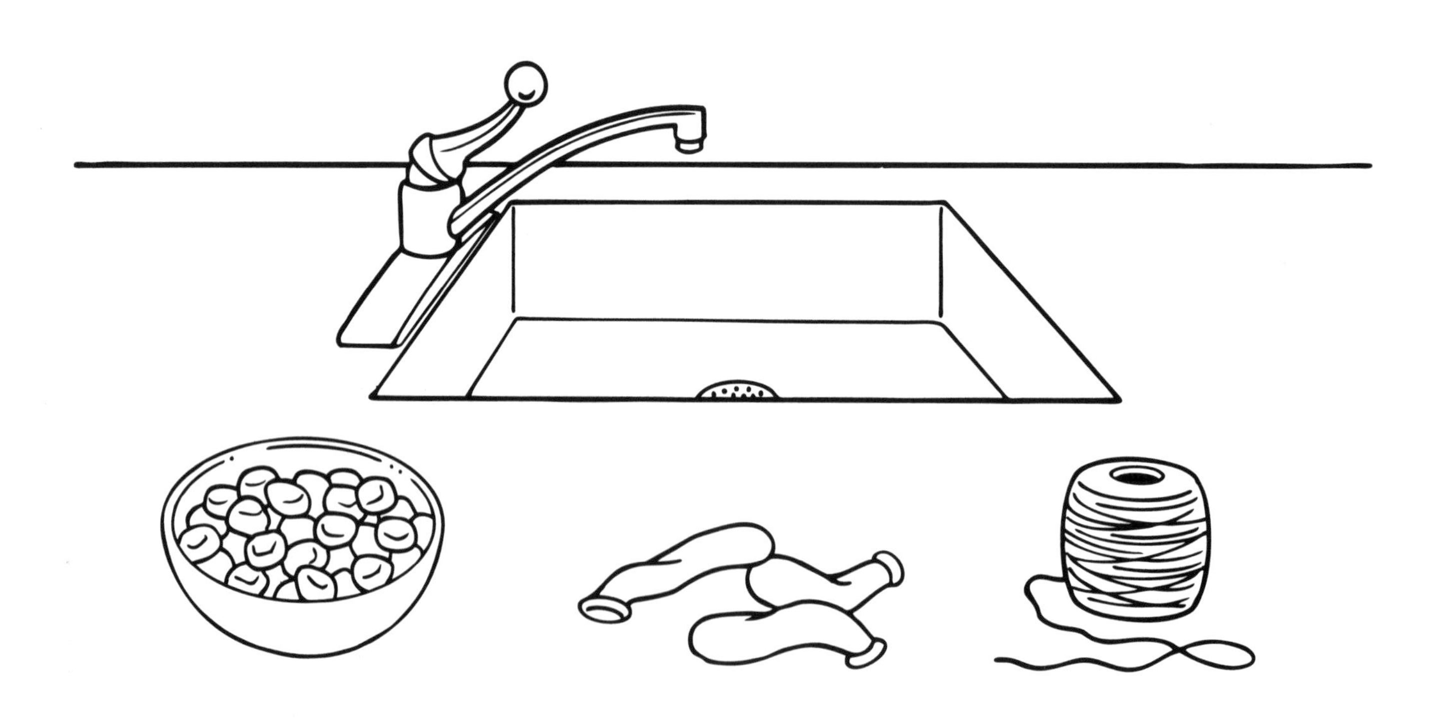

Static Electricity *(cont.)*

Getting Ready for the Activity

1. Make copies of the Science Journal page. Give one copy to each student.
2. Make copies of the Family Connection page. Give one copy to each student.
3. Reproduce word cards on cardstock (or heavy paper), laminate, and display.
4. Prepare the following stations prior to student participation. Determine how and when students will rotate (plan on 10 minutes per station). If water is not available, skip Experiment 2.

Station 1: Hair

- Hair Station Card
- balloons

Station 2: Water

- close proximity to a sink with a faucet
- Water Station Card
- balloons

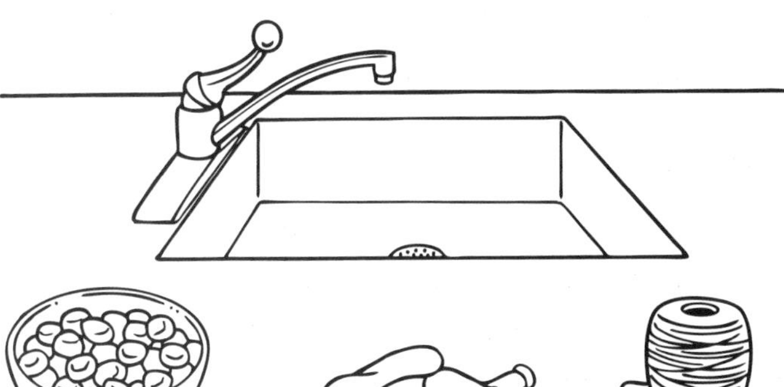

Station 3: Styrofoam

- bag of Styrofoam pieces
- Styrofoam Station Card
- balloons

Introduce the Activity

1. Read a book of your choice that reinforces the theme of static electricity. (**Suggestion:** *All About Electricity* by Melvin Berger)
2. Introduce the word cards for the unit. Discuss the meaning of new words and concepts.
3. Explain that the class will divide up into three groups and participate in three separate observation experiments. Each student will complete the experiments using the materials present at each station.
4. Describe the procedure for each of the experiments before having students break off into the three groups.
5. If appropriate, give each student a balloon. Have him or her blow it up and tie it off. Then, give each student a piece of string and have him or her tie it to the end of the balloon. Explain that the balloon will be used at all three stations. Some students may need help from an adult.

Static Electricity *(cont.)*

Procedure

Station 1: Hair

1. Rub the balloon on your hair.
2. Move the balloon near your partner's hair. Observe what happens.
3. Switch roles and repeat the experiment.
4. Record observations on the Science Journal page.

   Note: If a student isn't able to use his or her hair to charge the balloon, they can rub their balloon on the carpet or their clothing.

Station 2: Water

1. Turn on the faucet so there is a steady stream of cold water.
2. Rub the balloon on your hair for 10–15 seconds.
3. Move the balloon near the stream of water. Do not touch the balloon to the water.
4. Observe what happens to the stream of water as the balloon approaches. (The water should bend away from the balloon.)
5. Record observations on the Science Journal page.

Station 3: Styrofoam

1. Rub the balloon on your hair.
2. Move the balloon over the top of the Styrofoam pieces.
3. Observe what happens.
4. Record observations on the Science Journal page.

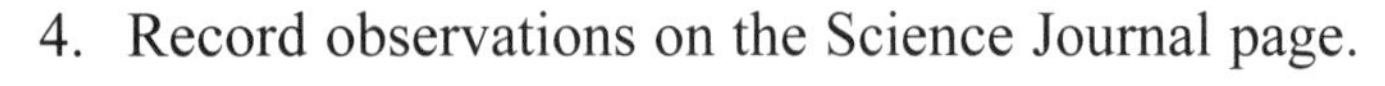

Family Connection

Send home the Family Connection page and ask students to complete it with their families.

Fun Science Questions and Facts

What is Static Electricity?

All materials contain millions of tiny particles called protons and electrons. Protons have positive charges, and electrons have negative charges. They usually balance each other, but when two surfaces rub together (friction), some of the electrons rub off one surface and attach to the other, creating static electricity. Materials with like charges move away from each other, and those with opposite charges are attracted to each other.

When I rub a balloon on my hair, why does it make my hair stand up?

When you rub a balloon on your hair, the electrons from each hair jump onto the balloon leaving each individual hair positively charged. The balloon is negatively charged, and since your hair is positively charged, your hair and the balloon are attracted to each other. Since *like* charges move away from each other, each positively charged hair is trying to move away from another positively charged hair and ends up standing straight up.

Why do I sometimes get a "shock" when I touch the doorknob?

You create static electricity by walking across the carpet, and when you touch the metal doorknob—ZAP! You pick up extra electrons from your shoes rubbing against the carpet. Once you touch the doorknob, the electrons leave you and jump to the doorknob. You will feel a little shock, and if it is dark, you will see a little spark as the electrons jump across the air to the doorknob.

Name ______________________________

Static Electricity

Station 1: Hair

Record what happened to your partner's hair during the experiment.

Station 2: Water

Record what the water looked like when you moved the balloon close to it.

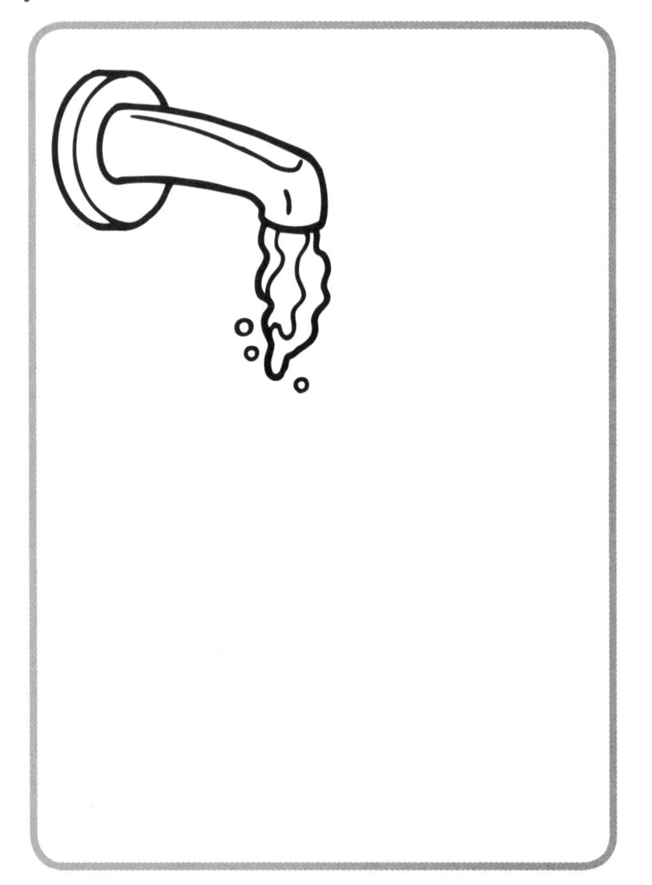

Station 3: Styrofoam

Record what you observed when you moved the balloon close to the Styrofoam pieces.

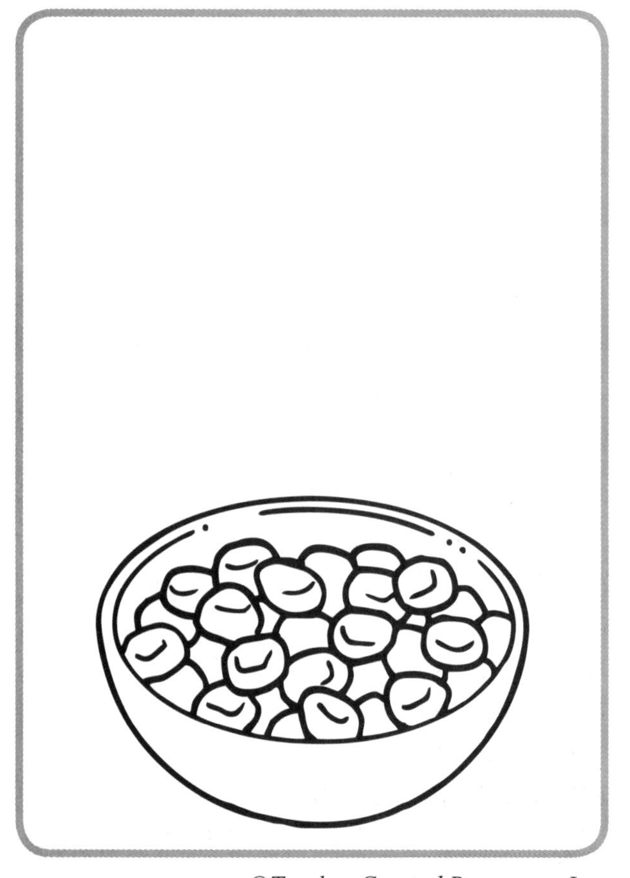

Name ____

Home School Connection

We are studying electricity. We are conducting experiments with static electricity. Prepare to be impressed!

Your child's assignment is to demonstrate and explain some of the experiments that were conducted in class. Please assist your child in blowing up and tying a balloon for these static electricity experiments.

Spend some time talking with your child about these questions.

- What does it mean to "charge" a balloon?
- What is the best method to charge the balloon?
- What happens if the balloon is not charged?
- What other objects can you charge and use to conduct these experiments?
- What is happening when the balloon makes your hair stand up?
- Why did the water bend away from the balloon?
- What is static electricity?

Did You Know?

All materials contain millions of tiny particles called *protons* and *electrons*. Protons have positive charges, and electrons have negative charges. They usually balance each other. But when two surfaces rub together, friction is created. Some of the electrons rub off one surface and attach onto the other, creating static electricity. Materials with like charges move away from each other. Materials with opposite charges are attracted to each other.

For example, when you rub a balloon on your hair, the electrons from each hair jump onto the balloon, leaving each individual hair positively charged. Since like charges move away from each other, each positively charged hair is trying to move away from another positively charged hair and ends up standing straight up. The balloon is negatively charged, and since your hair is positively charged, your hair and the balloon are attracted to each other. Since *like* charges move away from each other, each positively charged hair is trying to move away from another positively charged hair and ends up standing straight up.

balloon

charge

electricity

positive

negative

rub

shock

static

hair

string

water

Styrofoam

Hair
Water
Styrofoam

Fossils

Demonstration Materials

- 1/4 cup dry plaster mixture
- small pitcher of water
- measuring cups (1/8, 1/4)
- 8–12 oz. cup
- craft stick
- empty margarine container
- large bucket
- sand
- water
- permanent marker
- objects to use for imprinting (e.g., shells, small plastic animals, leaves, etc.)
- old toothbrush
- Science Journal—*Fossils* (page 103)
- Word Cards—*Fossils* (page 104)
- Station Cards—*Fossils* (page 105)

Student Materials

- dry plaster mixture (1/4 cup per student)
- small pitchers of water (1/8 cup per student)
- measuring cups
- 8–12 oz. cups (1 per student)
- craft sticks (1 per student)
- empty margarine containers (1 per group)
- damp sand
- permanent markers (1 per group)
- objects to use for imprinting (e.g., shells, small plastic animals, leaves, etc.)
- old toothbrushes (1–2 per group)
- Science Journal—*Fossils* (page 103)

Getting Ready for the Activity

1. Make copies of the Science Journal page. Give one copy to each student.
2. Reproduce word cards on cardstock (or heavy paper), laminate, and display.
3. Fill bucket with sand and add water to dampen. Sand should be damp, but not dripping wet.
4. Place the Station Cards at the three workstations: Preparing the Imprint, Making the Fossil, and Unearthing the Fossil.
5. Divide the class into small groups of 4–5 students. Plan to complete the fossil activity in these small groups over a period of a few days.

Fossils *(cont.)*

Introduce the Activity

1. Read a book of your choice that reinforces the theme of fossils. (**Suggestions:** *Fossils Tell of Long Ago* by Aliki; *Dinosaur Bones* by Aliki)
2. Introduce the word cards for the unit. Discuss the meaning of new words and concepts.
3. Demonstrate this experiment to the entire class. Follow the steps outlined below.

Procedure

Station 1: Preparing the Imprint

1. Choose the object you would like to use for your imprint.
2. Fill a margarine container half full of damp sand. Pat down the sand and smooth the surface.
3. Place your object inside the container. Press down halfway into the sand.
4. Lift the object out of the sand, being careful not to move it side to side. Lift it directly up and out of the sand.
5. Observe the imprint. If it is satisfactory, move to the next step. If not, repeat the above steps until you are happy with the imprint. Remember, your actual fossil will have many more details than you can see when looking at the imprint. The important thing to look for is that sand has not fallen into the imprint.

Fossils *(cont.)*

Procedure *(cont.)*

Station 2: Making the Fossil

1. Print your name on one end of a craft stick. Set aside.
2. Put 1/4 cup of plaster into a cup. Add 1/8 cup of water and mix with your craft stick. Be sure to hold your stick from the end with your name. Stir continuously until it is the consistency of pancake batter.
3. Pour the plaster mixture into the imprint you created in the sand. The plaster mixture will fill up the imprint and then cover the remaining surface of the sand inside the container. Stick your craft stick into the sand/plaster next to the edge of the container. Your name should be at the top of the stick. This will identify your fossil.

   Note: Depending on the size of the object used for the imprint, the amount of plaster needed to cover the imprint may need to be increased.

4. Set aside to dry. Quick-setting plaster can dry in a few hours. Regular plaster takes about 24 hours to dry.
5. Complete the Science Journal page by drawing a picture of what you think your fossil will look like when you unearth it.

Station 3: Unearthing the Fossil

1. Print your name on the plaster with a permanent marker.
2. Use the craft stick to carefully pry up the plaster and remove it from the container.
3. Use an old toothbrush and brush away the sand to reveal your fossil. (Stand over a trash can to reduce cleanup time.)
4. Observe your fossil. Record what it looks like on the bottom of your Science Journal page.

   Note: The containers of sand can be reused.

Fun Science Questions and Facts

Is this a real fossil?

No, for it to be a real fossil, parts of a once-living organism would have absorbed minerals over time and become like a rock.

What is this type of fossil called?

It is actually considered a *mold*, and the object that made the impression is called a *cast*.

How does the plaster get hard?

When water (H_2O) is added to the dry plaster mixture (hemihydrate of calcium sulfate–$2CaSO_4H_2O$), a chemical reaction along with crystallizations occur, resulting in a quick setting paste that dries to form a tough, hard solid.

How long does it take to make a fossil?

It depends on the conditions, but generally it takes a very long time (hundreds and even thousands of years) to make a fossil.

Why do scientists use fossils?

They learn about animals and plants that lived long ago by studying their fossil remains.

Have you ever seen a fossil?

Fossils are found all over the world. Many museums have fossils on display.

Name ____

Fossils

Draw a picture of what you think your fossil will look like.

Day 2

Look at your fossil and record what it looks like.

fossil

bone

plant

rock

imprint

fragile

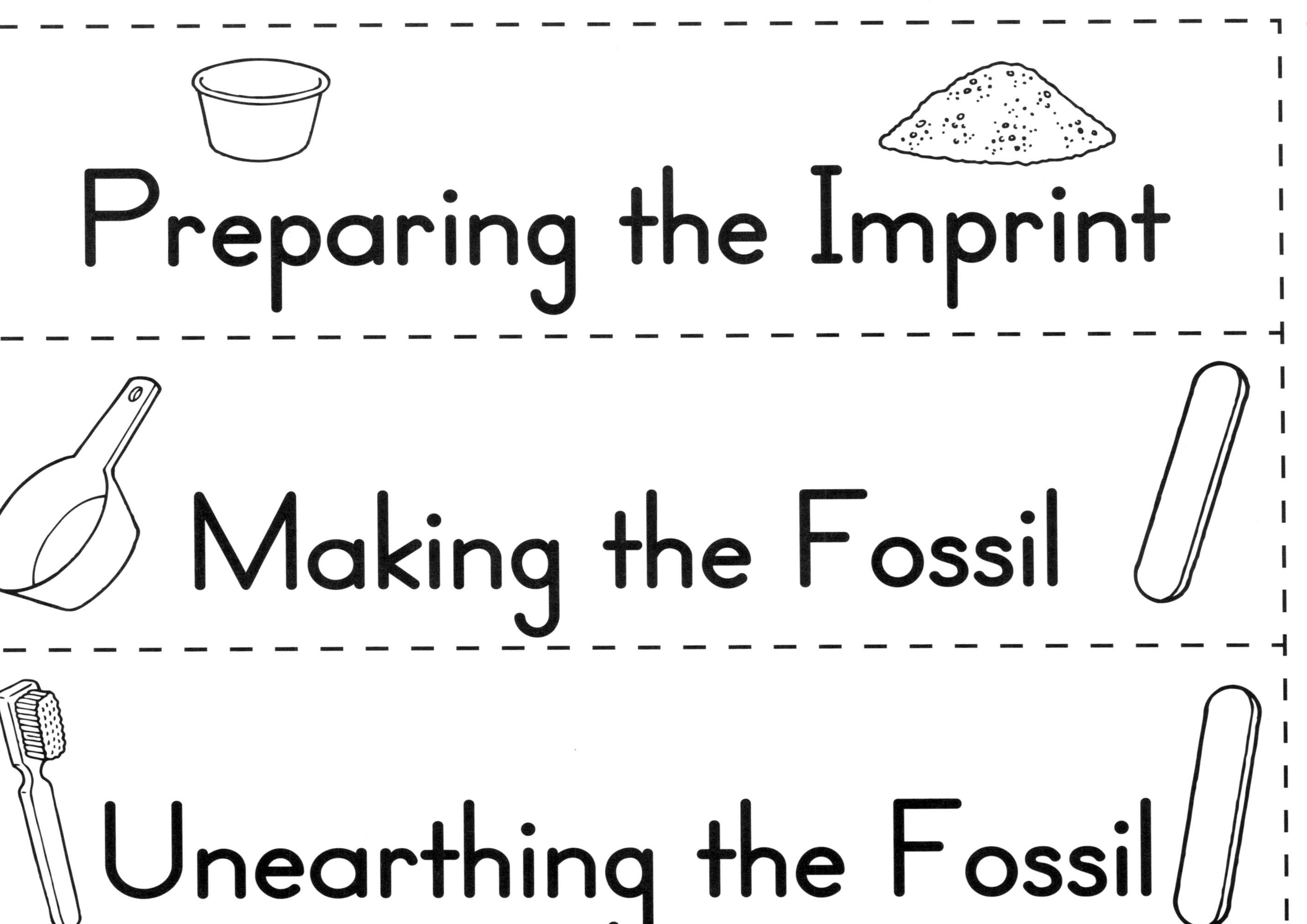
Preparing the Imprint
Making the Fossil
Unearthing the Fossil

Tooth Brushing Experiment

Demonstration Materials

- toothbrush
- toothpaste
- 1 hard-boiled egg (with white shell)
- 1 cup large enough for the egg to be completely submerged
- variety of sodas (orange, cola, grape, etc.)
- access to a sink or a dish tub of water
- spoon
- paper towels
- crayons and pencils
- Mini Book—*I Will Keep My Teeth Healthy!* (pages 110–112)
- Word Cards—*Tooth Brushing Experiment* (pages 114–115)

Student Materials

- old toothbrushes (2–3 per group)
- new toothbrushes (1 per student)
- toothpaste (2 tubes per group)
- hard-boiled eggs (1 per student)
- cups large enough for the egg to be completely submerged (1 per student)
- variety of colored sodas (orange, cola, grape, etc.)
- access to a sink or a dish tub of water
- spoons (1 per group)
- paper towels
- stickers, bookmarks, or other reward
- crayons and pencils
- Mini Book—*I Will Keep My Teeth Healthy!* (pages 110–112)
- Family Connection—*Tooth Brushing Experiment* (page 113)

Tooth Brushing Experiment *(cont.)*

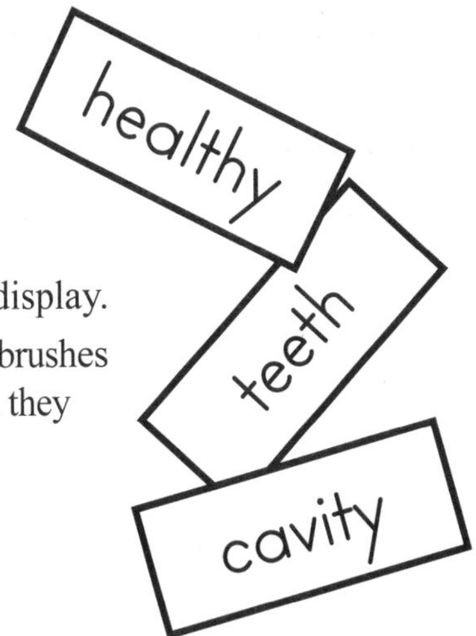

Getting Ready for the Activity

1. Make copies of the Family Connection page. Give one copy to each student.
2. Make copies of the Mini Book. Assemble each book prior to the activity. Give one copy to each student.
3. Reproduce word cards on cardstock (or heavy paper), laminate, and display.
4. Contact a local dentist or major toothpaste company. Request free toothbrushes and toothpaste. Most dentists will donate toothbrushes to a class. Often they will include information and additional dental hygiene supplies.
5. Hard-boil the eggs and cool.
6. Soak one egg in a cup of soda for at least 10 minutes.

Introduce the Activity

1. Read a book of your choice that reinforces the theme of dental hygiene. (**Suggestions:** *The Berenstein Bears Visit the Dentist* by Stan and Jan Berenstein; *Little Rabbit's Loose Tooth* by Lucy Bate)
2. Introduce the word cards for the unit. Discuss the meaning of new words and concepts.
3. Demonstrate this experiment to the entire class. Follow the steps outlined on the following page.

Tooth Brushing Experiment *(cont.)*

Procedure

1. Print your name on a cup.
2. Place a hard-boiled egg into your cup. Pour the soda into the cup until the egg is covered completely.
3. Complete the Mini Book. Color each page and add details as necessary to complete the pages.
4. After 10–15 minutes, return to your egg and carefully lift it out of the cup with a spoon. Place it on a paper towel.
5. Observe the egg. (Explain the similarities between the enamel on the egg and teeth enamel. Explain that our teeth are also affected by what we eat and drink.)
6. Use a toothbrush and toothpaste to brush the egg. Dip the toothbrush in water as necessary to completely clean the egg. (Discuss the importance of brushing teeth regularly to keep them clean and healthy.)
7. As a class, chorally read the Mini Book. Share with the class your favorite page.

Family Connection

Send home one new toothbrush and the Family Connection page with each student. Explain the process for checking off the boxes on the Family Connection page. Explain that when students complete it and bring it back they will receive a surprise, such as a sticker or bookmark.

Fun Science Questions and Facts

Is there really enamel on my tooth?

The shiny enamel on the visible part of teeth is the hardest material in the human body. It is the only material that is never exchanged or replaced.

What are the other parts of my tooth?

The enamel covers the dentin, which surrounds the pulp (the part with the nerves and blood vessels).

If I don't take care of my baby teeth, will it affect my permanent teeth?

Most permanent teeth are formed in the jaw near the roots of the baby teeth by the time children are 4 years old. Poor nutrition affects the formation of permanent teeth even before they are visible.

When should I go to the dentist?

As soon as a child has teeth, he or she should go to the dentist for regular checkups.

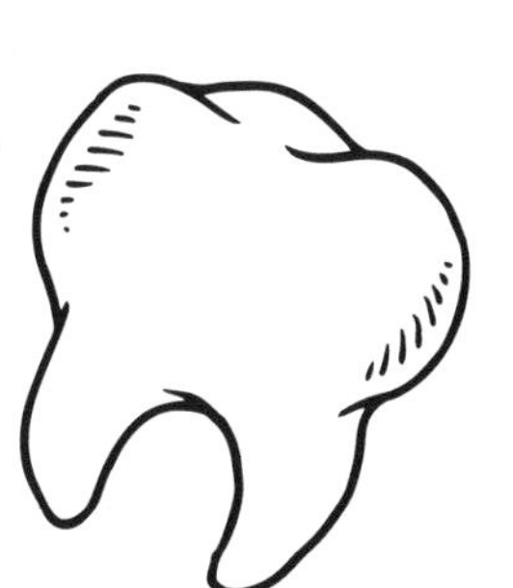

How many teeth will I have as an adult?

Most adults have 32 teeth.

When will my baby teeth start falling out?

Children have 20 baby teeth which start falling out when a child is between six and seven years old. The teeth are replaced by adult or permanent teeth.

Why has my friend lost her first tooth, and I haven't yet?

Everybody is different, but eventually, most children do start losing their baby teeth between the ages of six and seven years old.

When do babies get their teeth?

Some babies start to get their teeth when they are four or five months old, and others wait until they are almost a year old.

I Will Keep My Teeth Healthy!

By ______________________

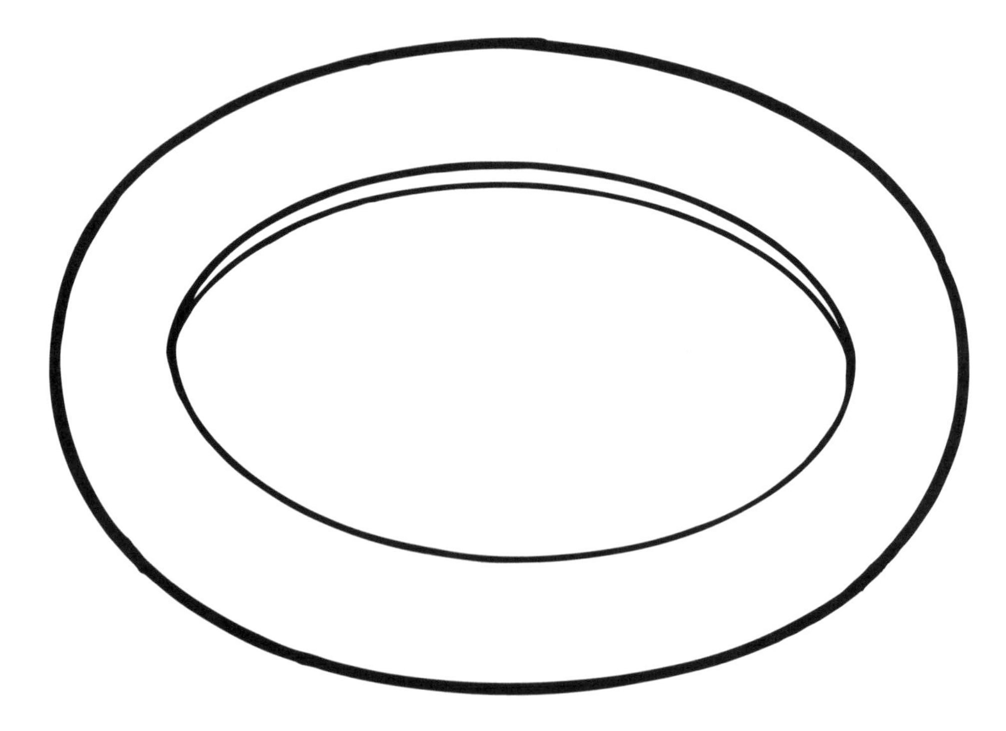

I will eat healthy food.

1

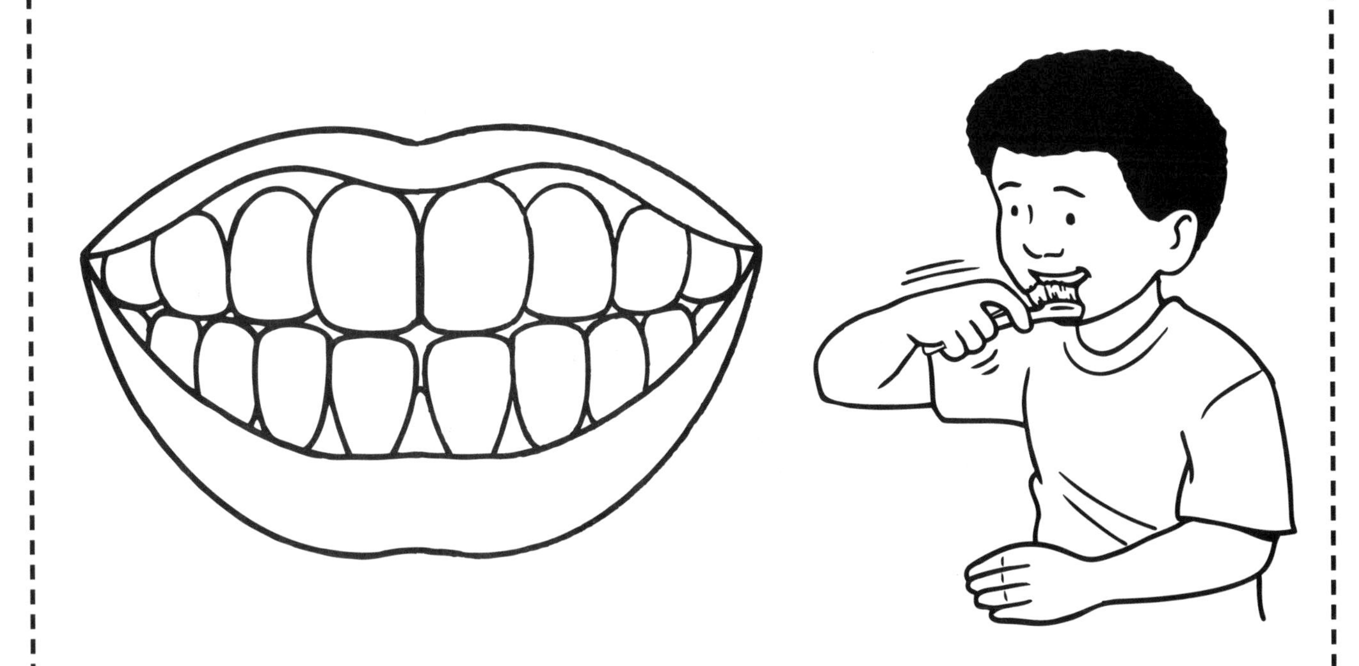

I will brush my teeth every morning
and every night.

I will ask an adult to help me floss my teeth. 3

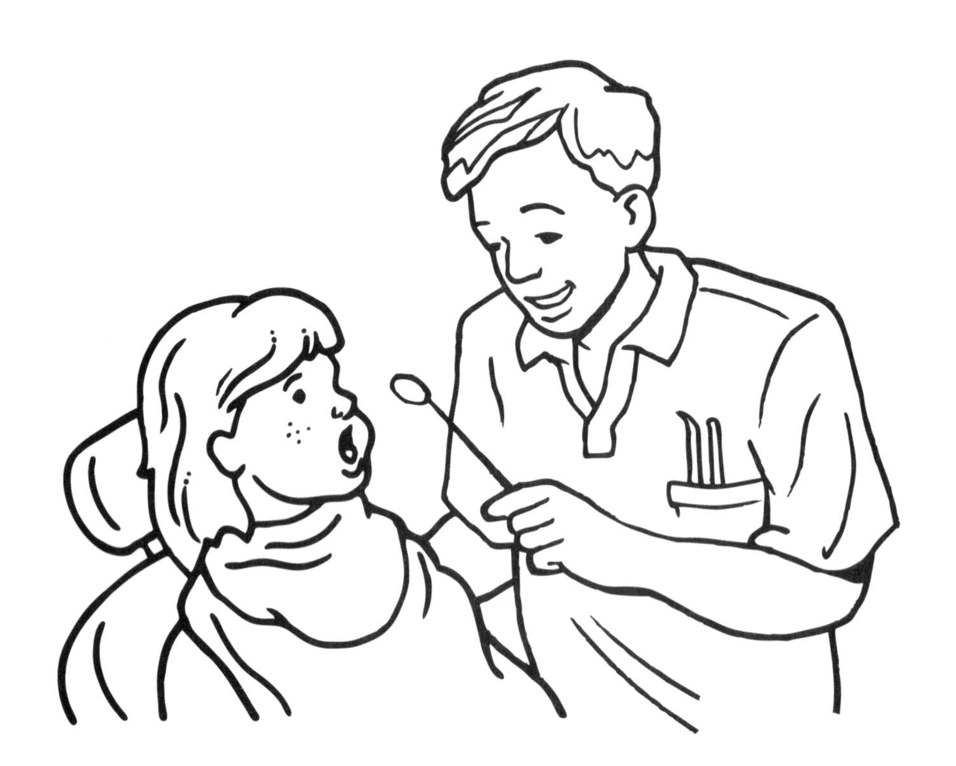

I will visit the dentist twice a year.

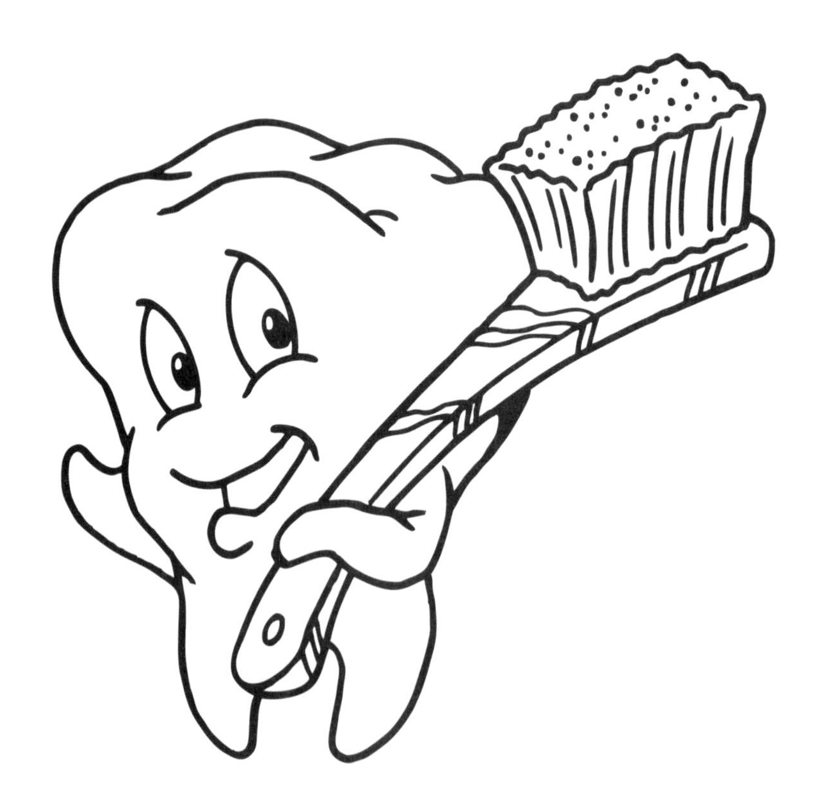

I will keep my teeth healthy!

Name ____

Home School Connection

We have been studying dental hygiene and how we can keep our teeth healthy. Today we performed an experiment to demonstrate the importance of brushing our teeth. Ask your child to tell you about the hard-boiled egg experiment performed in class today.

Your child has been given a new toothbrush to take home.

These toothbrushes were courtesy of

______________________________________ .

Please have your child use the chart below to record his or her tooth brushing habits for one week. When your child returns the chart to school, he or she will receive a special surprise.

NAME: ______________________________

DATE							
MORNING							
NIGHT							

tooth

toothpaste

floss

toothbrush

dentist

checkup

permanent

baby

healthy

cavity

enamel

teeth

Shadow Pole Time

Demonstration Materials

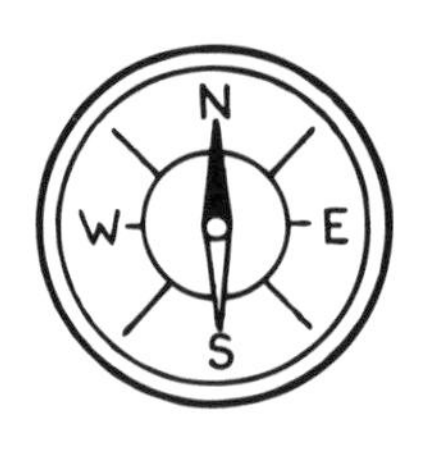

- yard or meter stick
- bucket or large tub
- sand
- chalk
- compass
- hard surface area, such as the blacktop
- pencil
- clipboard (or a 9" x 12" piece of heavy cardboard and a clothespin)
- demonstration clock (standard analog clock with hands)
- Science Journal—*Shadow Pole Time* (page 119)
- Word Cards—*Shadow Pole Time* (page 120)

Student Materials

- pencils
- clipboards (or 9" x 12" pieces of heavy cardboard and clothespins) (1 per student)
- analog clocks (1 for every 2 students)
- Science Journal—*Shadow Pole Time* (page 119)

Getting Ready for the Activity

1. Make copies of the Science Journal page. Give one copy to each student.
2. Reproduce word cards on cardstock (or heavy paper), laminate, and display.
3. Find a suitable area to conduct this experiment. It should be a hard surface that gets full sun all day.
4. Plan on taking 5–10 minutes at the beginning of each hour throughout the day to perform this experiment. (e.g., 8:00 A.M., 9:00 A.M., 10:00 A.M., and so on)

Shadow Pole Time *(cont.)*

Introduce the Activity

1. Read a book of your choice that reinforces the theme of shadows or time. (**Suggestions:** *Me and My Shadow* by Arthur Dorros; *What Makes A Shadow?* by Clyde Robert Bulla)
2. Introduce the word cards for the unit. Discuss the meaning of new words and concepts.
3. Demonstrate this experiment to the entire class. Follow the steps outlined below.

Procedure

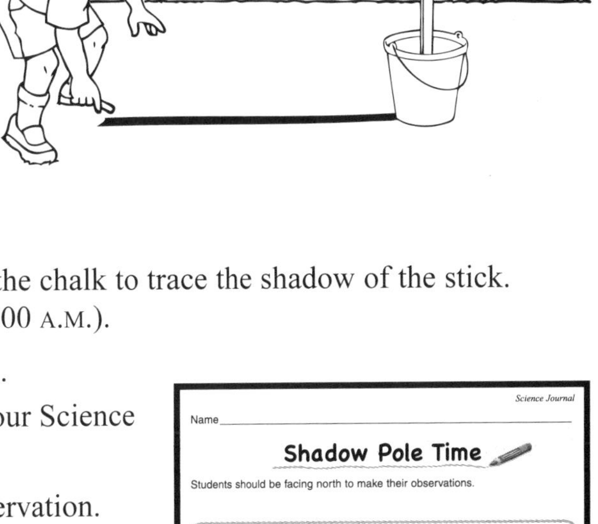

1. Print your name on the Science Journal page. Attach it to your clipboard.
2. Take the clipboards and pencils outside.
3. Fill the bucket with the sand. Take the bucket, yardstick, and chalk to the area where you will conduct the experiment.
4. Line up shoulder-to-shoulder facing north. Place the bucket with the yardstick (shadow pole) directly in front of you.

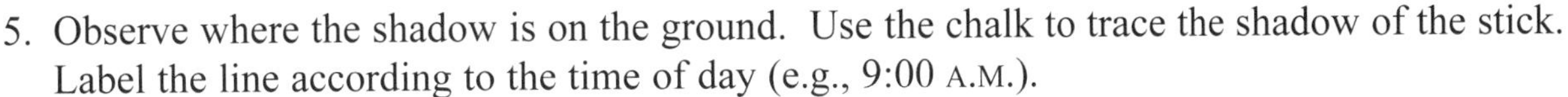

5. Observe where the shadow is on the ground. Use the chalk to trace the shadow of the stick. Label the line according to the time of day (e.g., 9:00 A.M.).
6. Leave the shadow pole and return to the classroom.
7. Record your observations of the first shadow on your Science Journal page.
8. Keep the clipboards handy for the next hourly observation.
9. Each hour return to the shadow pole and record the shadow. Make predictions about where the shadow will be the next hour. When you return to the classroom, compare the shadow lines with the hour hand on the clock. Use the small clocks to practice telling time.
10. After your last observation of the day, explain why the shadow moves each hour and how that relates to time.

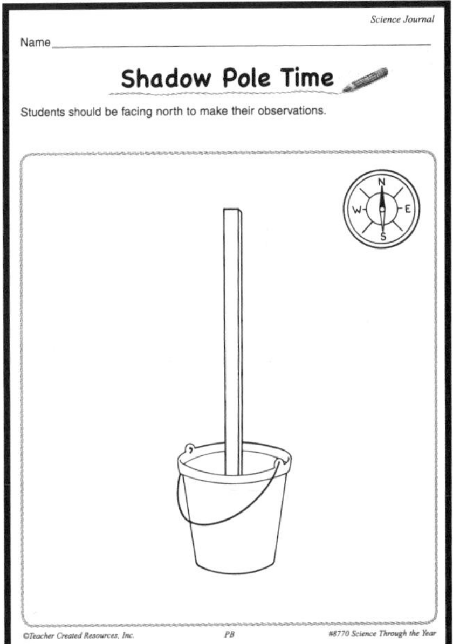

Science Journal

Name

Shadow Pole Time

Students should be facing north to make their observations.

©Teacher Created Resources, Inc. PB #8770 Science Through the Year

Fun Science Questions and Facts

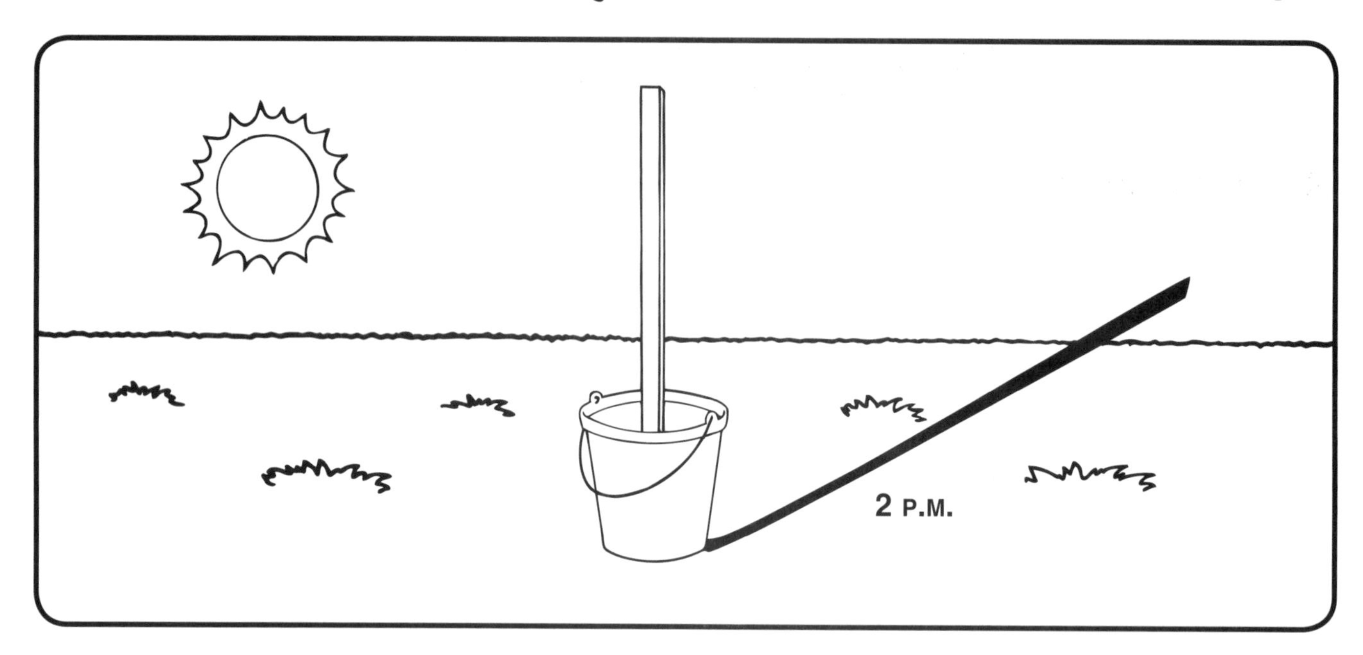

Why do we need to be facing north?

As the Earth rotates, it is revolving toward the East, and by facing north the shadows will represent passing time. If you faced south, the shadows would not represent the correct time on a clock. North is also the frame of reference for a compass.

Does the sun move? Why do we say the sun comes up and goes down?

Actually the sun is stationary, and Earth is orbiting around the sun. At the same time that Earth is orbiting, it is also rotating on its axis, which creates day and night. It may seem like the sun is moving, but the Earth moves, and the sun stays still in the center of our solar system.

Why are some shadows shorter than others?

As Earth moves and the sun is directly overhead, the shadows will be shorter. The longest shadows will be early in the morning and late in the afternoon.

Will the shadows be exactly where the corresponding hour hand is on the clock?

It should be close, but there are variables (seasonal changes in the tilt of Earth, whether or not you are facing exactly north) that may make the shadow off by a little.

Note: Daylight Savings time will make your shadow clock off by an hour.

What will happen if we don't make it out at the beginning of the hour?

It will still have a shadow, but it won't be as easy to see its relationship to the time on a clock if the shadows are not representing time on the hour.

Name ____

Shadow Pole Time

Students should be facing north to make their observations.

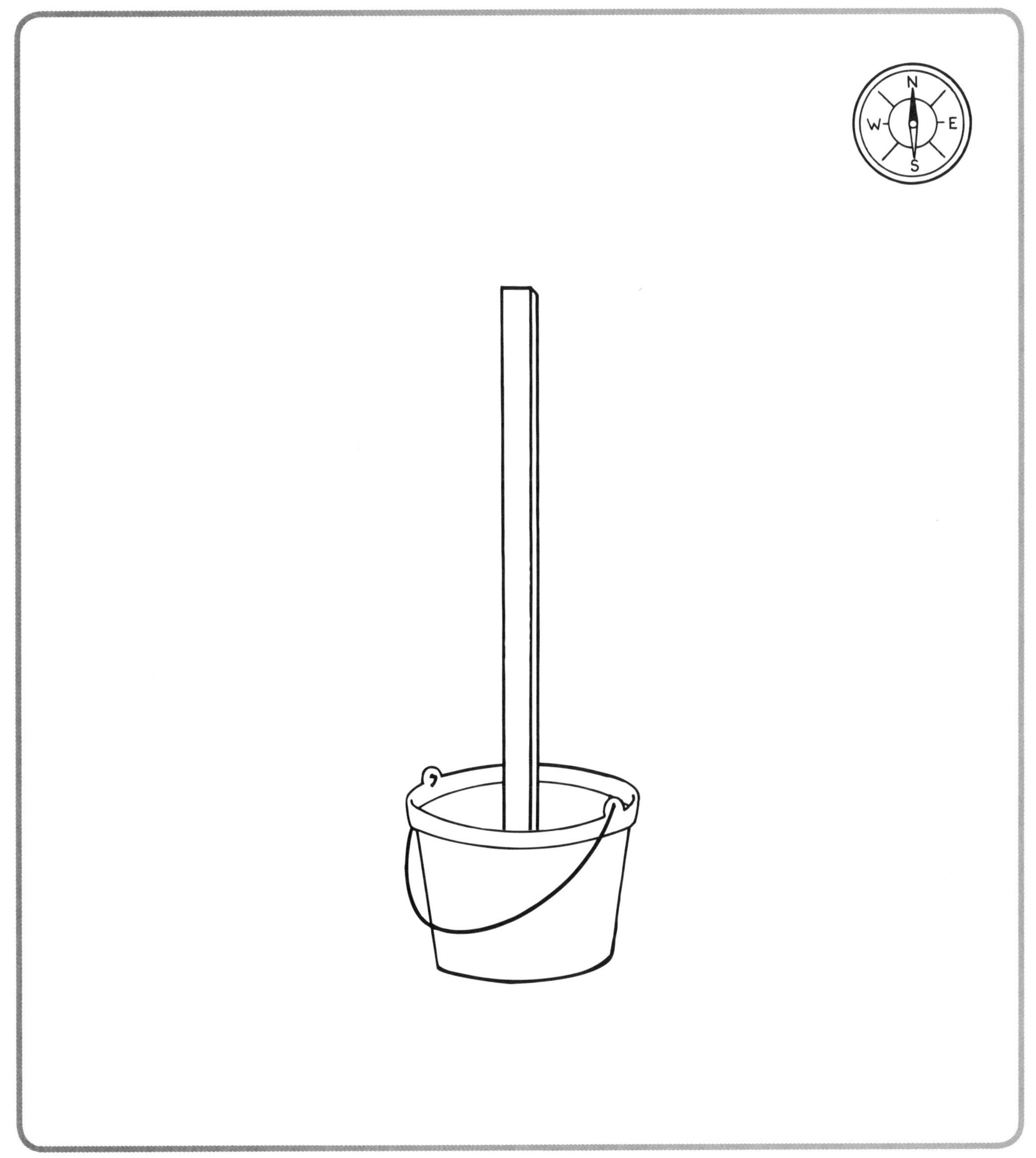

sun

shadow

north

time

hour

clock

Shadows

Demonstration Materials

- white crayon
- 2 pieces of black construction paper (9" x 12")
- glue or glue stick
- scissors
- tape
- small objects (e.g., stencils)
- white background for the projector (e.g., butcher paper or magnetic white boards)
- overhead projector
- Science Journal—*Shadows* (pages 125)
- Word Cards—*Shadows* (page 126–127)

Student Materials

- white crayons
- black construction paper (9" x 12") (2 per student)
- glue or glue sticks
- scissors
- tape
- small objects (e.g., stencils)
- flashlights (2 per group)
- boxes of varying sizes (2 per group)
- Science Journal—*Shadows* (pages 125)

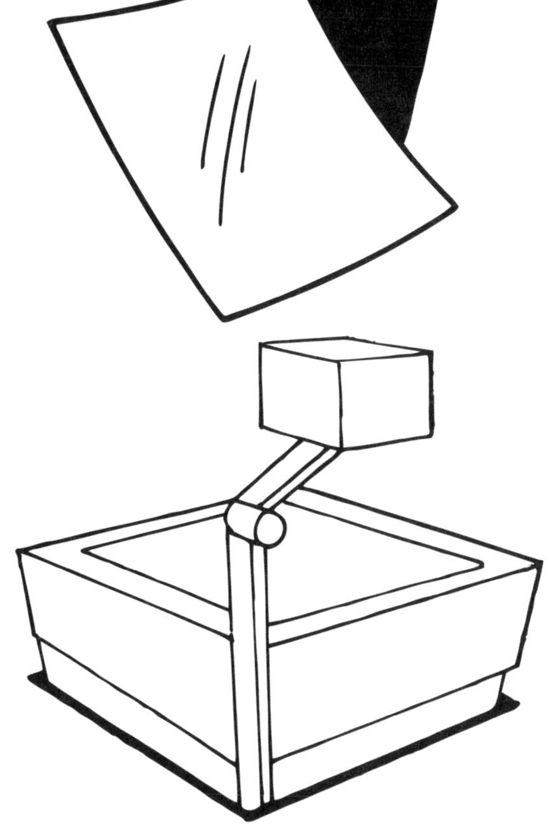

Shadows *(cont.)*

Getting Ready for the Activity

1. Make copies of the Science Journal page. Give one copy to each student.
2. Reproduce word cards on cardstock (or heavy paper), laminate, and display.
3. Set up the overhead to project onto a piece of white butcher paper taped to the wall or a magnetic white board.
4. Experiment with small items, choosing the ones that will make shadows that fit onto a 9" x 12" piece of paper.
5. Divide students into small groups. Have several flashlights and various sizes of boxes available for exploration while students wait for their turn to complete this experiment.
6. Place the Science Journal page, black construction paper, white crayons, glue or glue sticks, and scissors at each workstation.

Introduce the Activity

1. Read a book of your choice that reinforces the theme of shadows. (**Suggestions:** *Guess Whose Shadow* by Stephen R. Swinburne; *Nothing Sticks Like a Shadow* by Ann Tompert)
2. Introduce the word cards for the unit. Discuss the meaning of new words and concepts.
3. Demonstrate this experiment to the entire class. Follow the steps outlined on the next page.

Shadows *(cont.)*

Procedure

1. Print your name on the Science Journal page.
2. Choose an item to make a shadow. Place the item on the overhead projector. Attach a black piece of paper to the wall so that the shadow projects onto the paper.
3. Use a white crayon to trace the shadow onto the black paper.
4. Remove your black paper from the wall and your item from the overhead projector.

   CAUTION: Items moved on the projector will be difficult to line up again. Adult supervision, plus the rule that only the student who is tracing the object can touch it, helps avoid this problem.
5. Cut out your shadow and glue it onto the Science Journal page. Create a title for your shadow picture (e.g., **The Funny Fish**).
6. At the conclusion of this activity, share the shadow pictures with the class.

Fun Science Questions and Facts

What makes a shadow?

When light is blocked, shadows will appear. The overhead projector has a light bulb, and when the object is blocking the light, a shadow of the object appears on the wall.

What makes shadows big?

When a lot of light is blocked, the shadow will be bigger. If only a little light is blocked, the shadow will be smaller. Shadows in the morning and evening will be longer than shadows in the middle of the day when the sun is directly overhead.

What makes it dark at night?

Earth is always spinning or rotating on its axis as it orbits around the sun. When our part of Earth rotates away from the sun, a shadow is created because the sun's light is blocked.

Name ____

Shadows

Glue your shadow onto this page. Add a title and details to your picture.

project

morning

orbit

spin

rotate

Earth

light

dark

shadow

sun

day

night

Magnetism Experiment

Demonstration Materials

- several types of magnets (e.g., wand, horseshoe, bar, refrigerator, clips, etc.)
- paperclip, pencil, key, eraser, book, pair of scissors, crayon, magnet
- clipboard
- Science Journal—*Magnetism Experiment* (page 131)
- Word Cards—*Magnetism Experiment* (page 133)

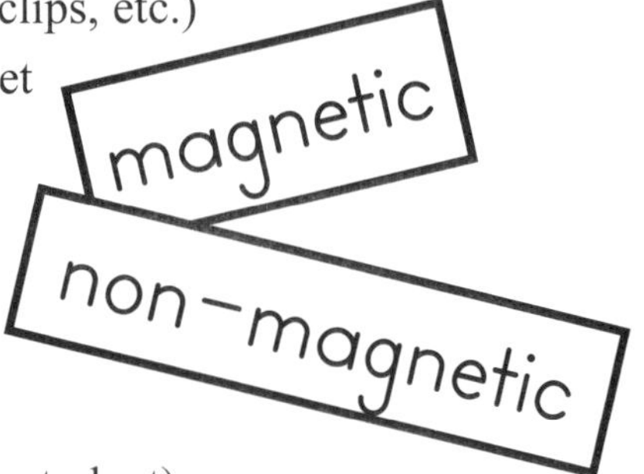

Student Materials

- magnets (e.g., wand, horseshoe, bar, refrigerator, clips, etc.) (1 per student)
- paperclip, pencil, key, eraser, book, pair of scissors, crayon, magnet (1 of each item per group)
- clipboards (1 per group)
- pencils (1 per student)
- Science Journal—*Magnetism Experiment* (page 131)
- Family Connection—*Magnetism Experiment* (page 132)

Getting Ready for the Activity

1. Make copies of the Science Journal page. Give one copy to each student.
2. Make copies of the Family Connection page. Give one copy to each student.
3. Reproduce word cards on cardstock (or heavy paper), laminate, and display.
4. Gather a variety of magnetic and non-magnetic items (see list above).
5. Place the pencils and clipboards at each workstation.

Magnetism Experiment *(cont.)*

Introduce the Activity

1. Read a book of your choice that reinforces the theme of magnetism. (**Suggestions**: *What Makes a Magnet?* by Franklyn M. Branley; *What Magnets Can Do* by Allan Fowler)
2. Introduce the word cards for the unit. Discuss the meaning of new words and concepts.
3. Demonstrate this experiment to the entire class. Follow the steps outlined below.

Procedure

1. Print your name on the Science Journal page.
2. Choose a magnet and then find the items listed on the Science Journal page.
3. Move the magnet near the first item, a paperclip. Observe to see if the item is attracted to the magnet. Record your observation on the Science Journal page. Mark an X in the **Yes** column or **No** column.
4. Repeat the above steps to complete the Science Journal page. Each student chooses two additional items (numbers 9 and 10) on which to perform the experiment. Draw the item or print the name of the item on the Science Journal page and mark an X in the **Yes** column or in the **No** column.

Family Connection

Send home the Family Connection page and ask students to complete it with their families.

Fun Science Questions and Facts

Why do some metal items stick to the magnet and some don't?

Magnetism is a special property that is found in a few metals, primarily in iron, but also in cobalt and nickel. Anything that has iron (or cobalt or nickel) in it will be attracted to a magnet, and anything that does not have iron will not be attracted to a magnet. A soda can is made of aluminum and because it does not have iron, it won't be attracted to a magnet.

Are all magnets the same?

Every magnet has a north pole and a south pole, regardless of the size of the magnet. Magnets come in all types of shapes and sizes (rings, bars, arcs, rods, and discs). A magnet can be broken into very small pieces, and each piece will have a north pole and a south pole.

What are magnets used for?

Magnets are used for lifting, separating, holding, and handling materials. Magnets are also used in a compass, which helps people identify which direction they are going.

How are magnets used in your home? In the classroom?

They are used to hold notes, to close cabinet doors, in paper clip holders, to hold up posters, etc.

How are magnetism and electricity related?

Moving electrons create magnetic fields around themselves. Since electricity is the movement of electrons, there is a definite relationship between electricity and magnetism. In most kinds of materials, the electrons spin in such a way as to cancel each other out, and the material is not magnetic. Iron is different because the electrons in iron spin together, and the entire piece of iron is magnetic.

What are magnets made from?

There are ceramic magnets, alnico magnets, rare earth magnets, and flexible magnets (rubber-like).

Name ______________________________

Magnetism Experiment

Is the item attracted to a magnet?

	Item	Yes	No
1.	paperclip		
2.	pencil		
3.	key		
4.	book		
5.	eraser		
6.	scissors		
7.	crayon		
8.	magnet		
9.			
10.			

Name ____

Home School Connection

We are studying magnetism. We have been conducting experiments in class to discover which objects are attracted to a magnet. Your child has brought home a magnet to use to complete this experiment. Please return the magnet when you complete this Family Connection activity.

Spend some time talking with your child about these questions.

- What does it mean if something is magnetic?
- Name a few common examples of items that are attracted to a magnet.
- What type of metal is attracted to a magnet?

Your child's assignment is to demonstrate and complete the following experiment by choosing items found in your home. Please assist your child in completing the magnetism experiment and recording his or her observations on the chart below.

Is the item attracted to a magnet?

	Item (draw or print)	Yes	No
1.			
2.			
3.			
4.			
5.			

Did You Know?

A magnet can be many sizes and shapes. It always has a north and south pole. Magnets are used in compasses to determine which direction you are going. Magnets are attracted to iron. Magnets have many uses in the manufacturing and handling of a wide variety of products.

magnet

attract

metal

iron

magnetic

non-magnetic

Pencil and Bag Experiment

Demonstration Materials

- plastic resealable sandwich bag
- pencil (round, not hexagonal)
- pitcher of water
- Science Journal—*Pencil and Bag Experiment* (page 138)
- Word Cards—*Pencil and Bag Experiment* (page 140)

Student Materials

- plastic resealable sandwich bags (1 per student)
- round pencils (1 per student)
- pitchers of water (1 per workstation)
- Science Journal—*Pencil and Bag Experiment* (page 138)
- Family Connection—*Pencil and Bag Experiment* (page 139)

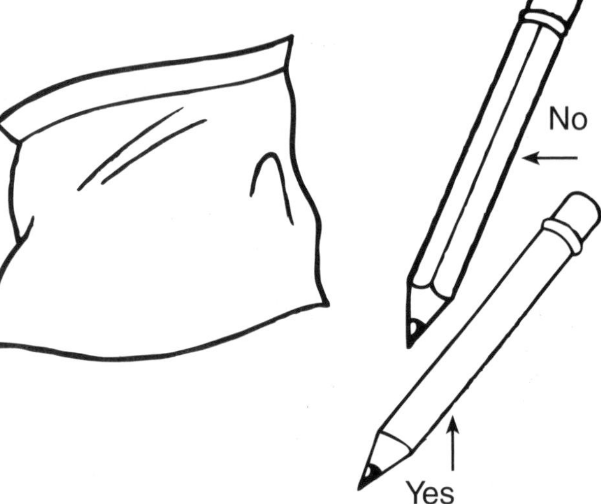

Getting Ready for the Activity

1. Make copies of the Science Journal page. Give one copy to each student.
2. Make copies of the Family Connection page. Give one copy to each student.
3. Reproduce word cards on cardstock (or heavy paper), laminate, and display.
4. Place one small pitcher of water at each workstation.
5. Sharpen round pencils and place at each workstation. Remember, pencils cannot have flat sides, they must be smooth.

   Caution: To avoid an injury, take extra care when using the sharpened pencils.
6. Choose an outside area to move to when you have your bags filled and sealed. This will help to reduce clean up.

Introduce the Activity

1. Read a book of your choice that reinforces the theme of experiments or polymers. (**Suggestions:** *What Are Atoms?* by Lisa Trumbauer; *Everyone Is a Scientist* by Lisa Trumbauer)
2. Introduce the word cards for the unit. Discuss the meaning of new words and concepts.
3. Demonstrate this experiment to the entire class. Follow the steps outlined on the next page.

sharpened

plastic

Pencil and Bag Experiment *(cont.)*

Procedure

1. Open the sandwich bag and fill it half full of water. Seal the bag.
2. Take the bags of water and sharpened pencils outside.
3. Hold the bag from the top with one hand and thrust the pencil through the bottom of the bag with your other hand. Be sure to keep the pencil moving through the bag until the point exits the other side of the bag. The ends of your pencil should be sticking out of the bag.

Safety Note: Make certain the pencil is pointing away from you when you poke it through.

4. Observe what happens. Draw a picture of it on your Science Journal page.
5. Hold the bag over the sink or outside over grass and remove the pencil.

Family Connection

Give each student a copy of the Family Connection page, one plastic sandwich bag, and a sharpened pencil. Ask students to complete the Family Connection page with their families.

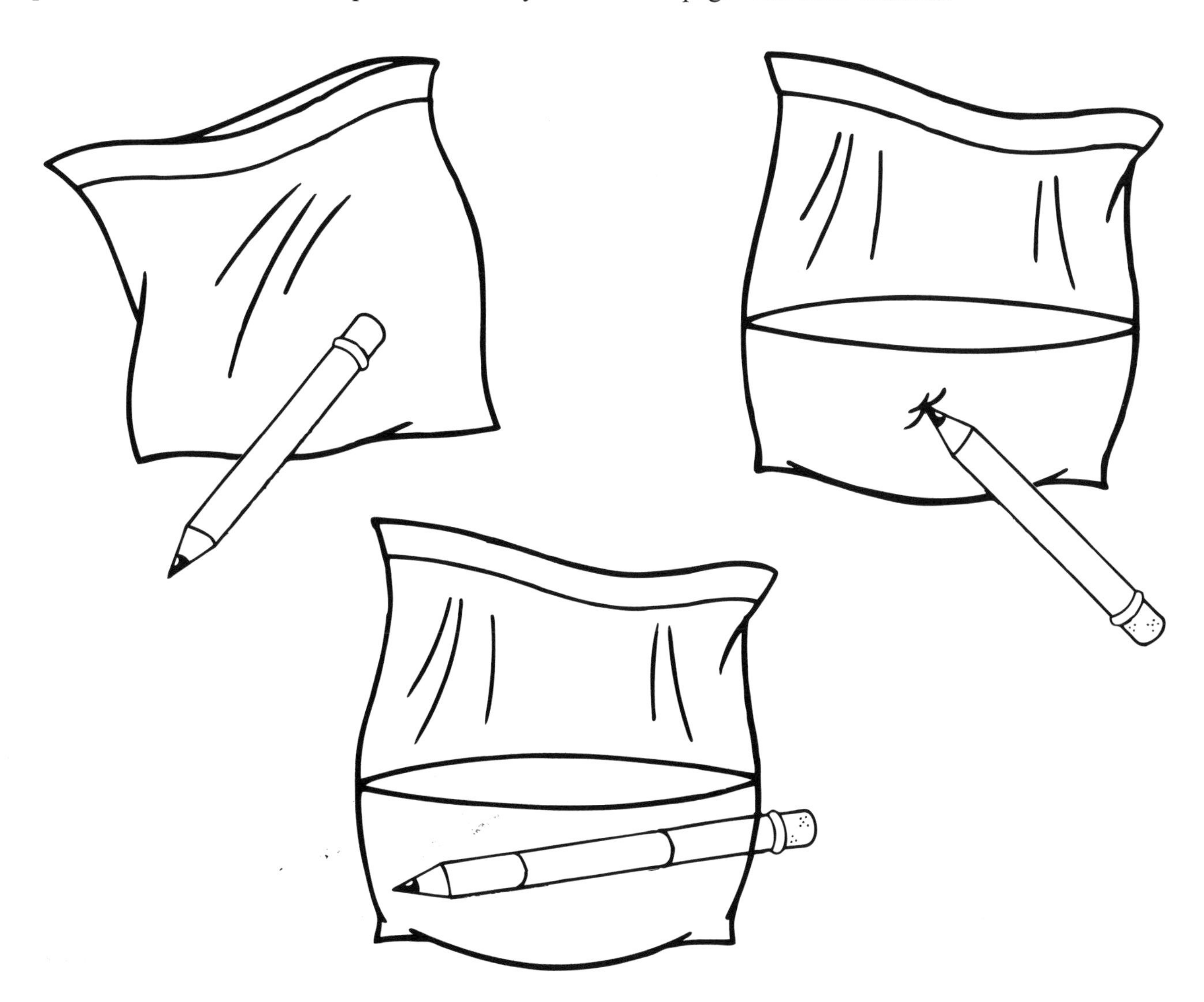

Pencil and Bag Experiment *(cont.)*

Procedure *(cont.)*

Polymer Demonstration

1. Explain that a polymer is a long chain of molecules.
2. To illustrate what this chain may look like, have 5–6 students stand next to each other without touching. Each of the students in the line represent a single molecule.
3. Ask the students to hold hands. Now the students represent a polymer.
4. To further illustrate this concept, have one group hold hands (polymer) and one group stand separately (single molecules). Send a student to run through each group.
5. The polymer group will be much harder to get by than the molecule group. This demonstrates how the polymer forms a seal due to its configuration.

Fun Science Questions and Facts

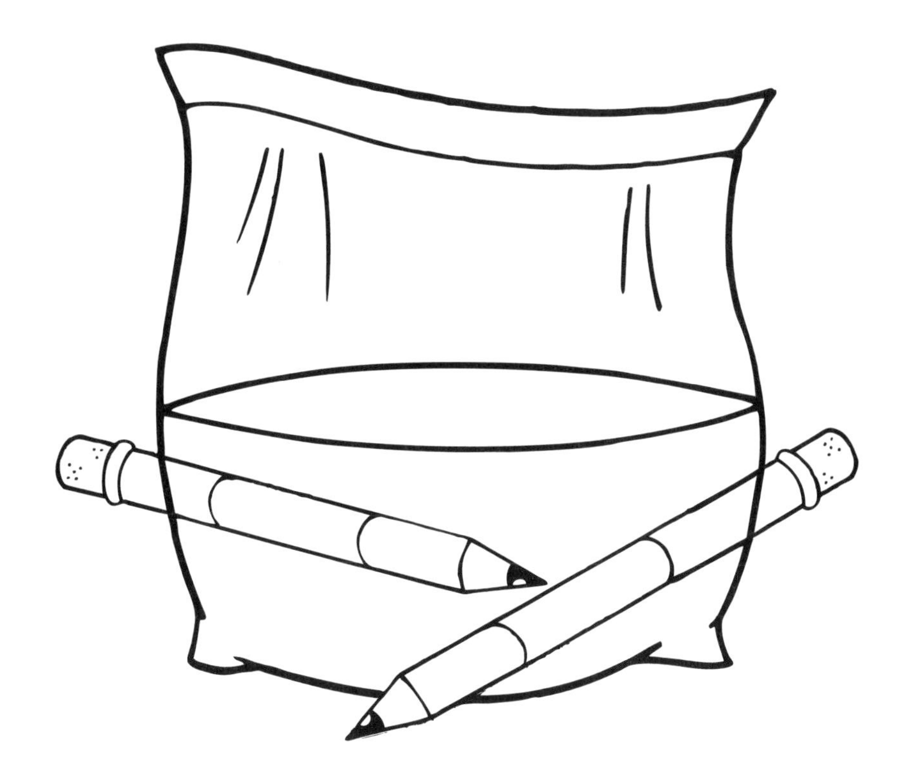

Why doesn't the water come out?

Plastic is stretchy because it is made out of polymers, which are long chains of molecules. The sharpened pencil is able to squeeze between the molecule chains and then the long chain of molecules seal themselves around the pencil.

What would happen if another pencil was stuck through the bag?

As long as it is a round pencil and there is room in the bag, you can stick several pencils into the bag and get the same result.

What else could I use to stick through the bag?

You can use any smooth object with a point on one end. A wooden skewer works well.
Note: Put some lotion or soap on the point first, so it doesn't snag the plastic.

What if I used a pencil that does not have rounded edges? Why?

Using an object that is not round will not allow the chain of molecules to seal itself around the object. Guess what the result will be.

Name ______________________________

Pencil and Bag Experiment

Draw a picture of what you observed during this experiment.

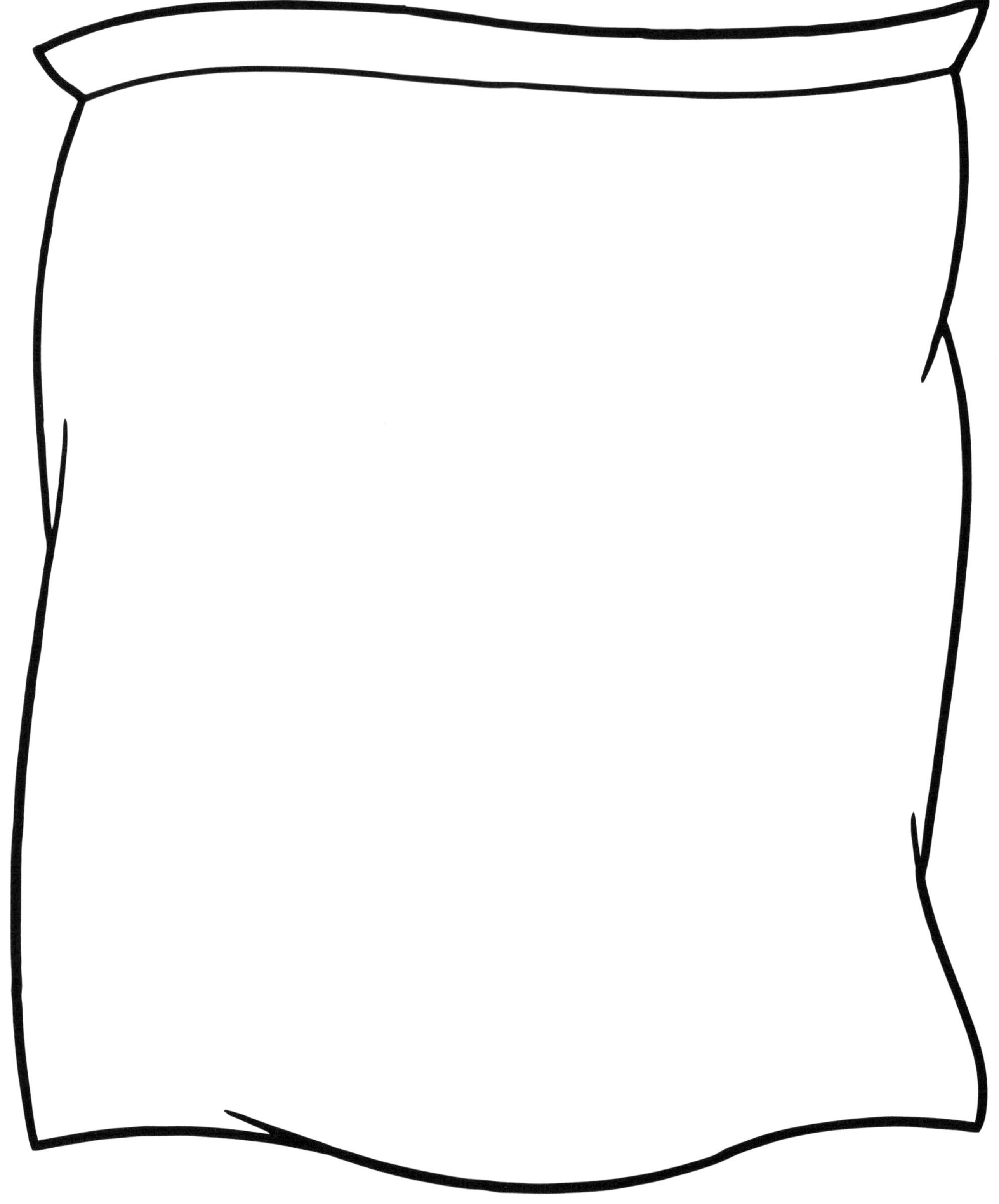

Name ____

Home School Connection

We have been conducting experiments in class to observe the properties of a *polymer*. Your child has been given a plastic sandwich bag and a sharpened pencil to perform this experiment.

Spend time talking with your child about these questions.

- What does it mean if something is a polymer?
- Name a few common examples of polymer we use every day.
- What is this sandwich bag made out of?

Your child's assignment is to demonstrate and explain one of the experiments that we conducted in class. Please assist him or her in filling up a small plastic sandwich bag halfway with water.

Hold the bag from the top with one hand. Then, thrust the pencil through the water filled part of the bag with your other hand. Be sure to keep the pencil moving through the bag (swift poke) until the point exits the other side of the bag. Both ends of your pencil should be sticking out of the water filled portion of the bag.

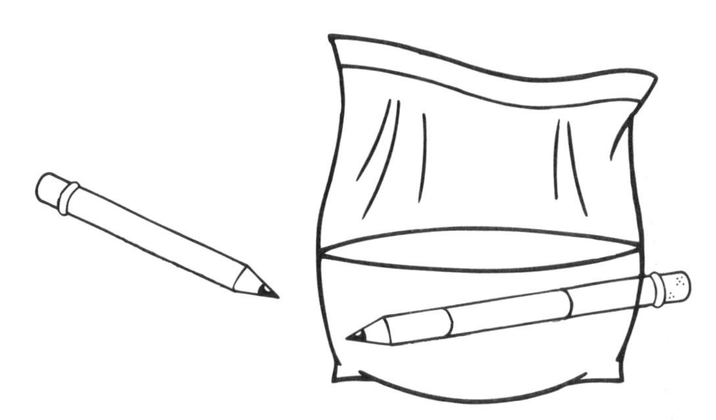

You can add more pencils to the bag and experiment with other objects. Be sure to have your bag in the sink or outside when you remove the pencils.

Did You Know?

A *polymer* is a large chain of molecules that are linked together. The links between the molecules are strong and like to stay together. When the pencil is pushed through the polymer (plastic bag), the links will surround the pencil and seal the bag.

polymer

plastic

halfway

sharpened

rounded

chain

Air Tube Experiment

Demonstration Materials

- diaper system refill bags which come in a roll and can be cut to whatever length is needed. (The long submarine-type sandwich bags found at sandwich shops also work.)
- scissors
- pencil
- permanent marker
- Science Journal—*Air Tube Experiment* (page 144)
- Word Cards—*Air Tube Experiment* (page 146–147)

Student Materials

- precut, 36" plastic "tube bags" (1 per student)
- permanent markers (1–2 per group)
- pencils (1–2 per group)
- Science Journal—*Air Tube Experiment* (page 144)
- Family Connection—*Air Tube Experiment* (page 145)

Getting Ready for the Activity

1. Make copies of the Science Journal page. Give one copy to each student.
2. Make copies of the Family Connection page. Give one copy to each student.
3. Reproduce word cards on cardstock (or heavy paper), laminate, and display.
4. Give each student a 36" diaper system refill bag. Tie a knot in one end of the plastic, creating a tube-shaped bag.
5. Place the permanent markers and pencils at each workstation.

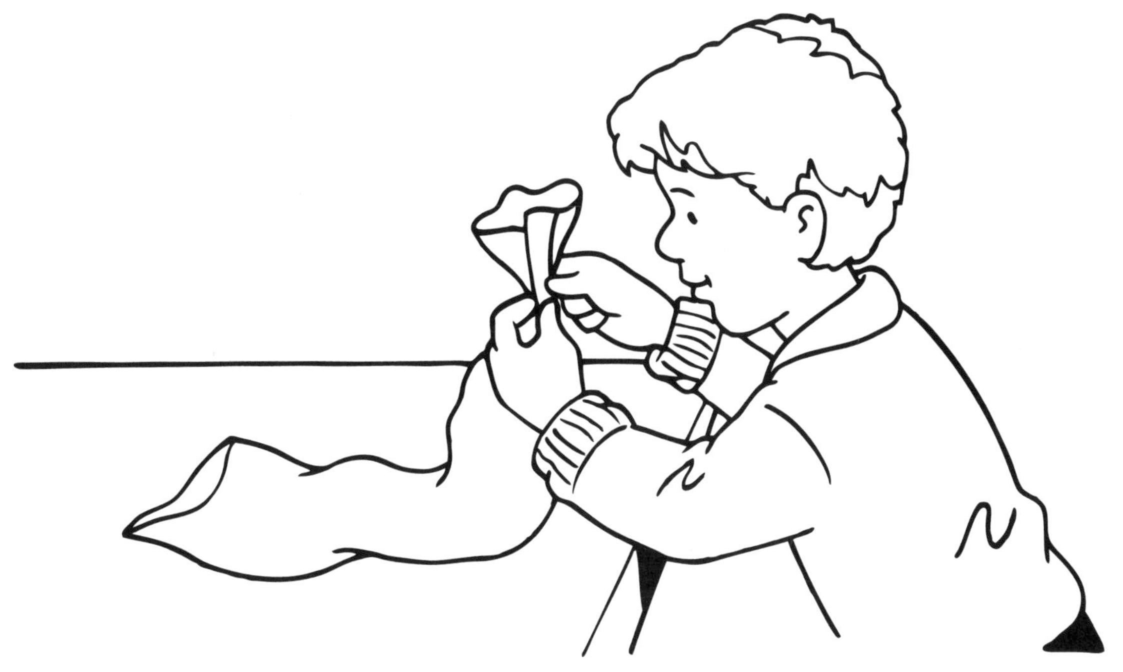

Air Tube Experiment *(cont.)*

Introduce the Activity

1. Read a book of your choice that reinforces the theme of air pressure or wind. (**Suggestions:** *The Wind Blew* by Pat Hutchins; *Feel the Wind* by Arthur Dorros)
2. Introduce the word cards for the unit. Discuss the meaning of new words and concepts.
3. Demonstrate this experiment to the entire class. Follow the steps outlined below. Choose a partner to help during your demonstration.

Procedure

1. Use a permanent marker to print your name on the plastic tube. Tie one end closed.
2. While one partner holds the bottom (closed end), the other partner blows into the open end of the long bag. This should be done by holding the bag with both hands an arm's length away from your mouth. Your lips should not be touching the bag. When the bag is full, close it.

3. Take turns blowing up your bag. See if you can blow it up with one breath. (**Note:** Students should hold the open end of the bag with *both* hands. In the picture above, the girl's right arm is not visible to allow "breath" to be illustrated.
4. Draw a picture illustrating this experiment on your Science Journal page.

Family Connection

Send home the air-tube bag and the Family Connection page. Ask students to complete the Family Connection page with their families.

Fun Science Questions and Facts

Why does the bag blow up quicker if I don't hold it against my mouth?

Fast moving air creates low pressure, which, when given the opportunity, will pull in the higher pressure air that surrounds it. If you hold the bag to your mouth, the high pressure air can't get in the bag. When you hold the bag away and blow into the bag, the high pressure air is also pulled into the bag.

Who is the scientist who discovered this principle of moving air?

Daniel Bernoulli performed a series of experiments in 1738. He is credited with discovering that fast moving air creates an area of low pressure which will pull in the surrounding high pressure air.

How does air pressure affect us?

When you listen to the news and the weatherman says there is a low pressure area, it means that the air is moving quickly and pulling in the surrounding air to create unstable weather (storms).

Do firefighters use air pressure at fire scenes to help them with their job?

It is common for firefighters to position fans, leaving a space between the source of air and the fan. The fast moving air (low pressure) draws in the surrounding air (high pressure) and creates a "positive air flow" which is a quick and efficient way to force smoke out of a building.

Name____

Air Tube Experiment

Draw a picture of what you observed during this experiment.

Your breath creates low pressure inside the bag. The high pressure air outside is pulled toward the low pressure air inside the bag.

Name ______________________________

Home School Connection

We have been conducting experiments in class to explore air pressure. Your child has brought home an "air tube" to use to complete this experiment.

Your child's assignment is to have each family member try to blow up the air tube and count their breaths. Then, your child will demonstrate the experiment and teach you how to blow up the air tube with just one breath. Each family member will try again with a partner and record his or her number of breaths the second time.

Air Tube Experiment

	Family Member	Number of breaths before instructions	Number of breaths after instructions
1.			
2.			
3.			

Did You Know?

Fast moving air creates low pressure, which when given the opportunity, will pull in the higher pressure air that surrounds it. If you hold the bag to your mouth, the high pressure air can't get in the bag. When you hold the bag away and blow into the bag, the high pressure is also pulled into the bag, filling it up more quickly.

Daniel Bernoulli performed a series of experiments in 1738 and is credited with discovering that fast moving air creates an area of low pressure which will pull in the surrounding high pressure air.

Weather reports often refer to air pressure. When there is low pressure, it means rain or a storm may be approaching. High pressure usually means fair weather.

air

high pressure

low pressure

away

against

pull

fast

slow

breath

inside

outside

tube

Seed Sprouter

Demonstration Materials

- clear, double CD case
- variety of seeds
- coffee filter
- spray bottle
- permanent marker
- large rubber band
- ruler
- 4 oz. plastic condiment cup
- scissors
- magnifying lens
- Mini Book—*Seed Sprouter* (pages 152–156)
- Word Cards—*Seed Sprouter* (page 158)

Student Materials

- clear, double CD case (1 per student)
- variety of seeds
- coffee filters (1 per student)
- spray bottles
- permanent markers
- large rubber bands (1 per student)
- rulers
- 4 oz. plastic condiment cups (1 per student)
- magnifying glass
- Mini Book—*Seed Sprouter* (pages 152–156)
- Parent Letter—*Seed Sprouter* (page 157)

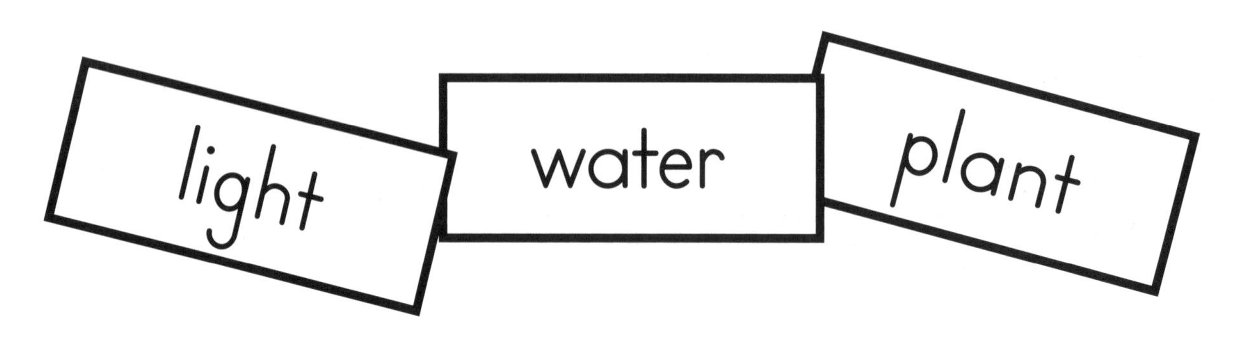

Seed Sprouter *(cont.)*

Getting Ready for the Activity

1. Make copies of the Mini Book. Assemble each book prior to the activity. Give one book to each student.
2. Reproduce word cards on cardstock (or heavy paper), laminate, and display.
3. Make copies of the Parent Letter. Send it home with students prior to the activity.
4. Collect a variety of seeds and the CD cases prior to the activity.
5. Remove the trays from the inside of the CD cases.
6. Turn the condiment cups upside down and cut a slit in the bottom. The slit should be wide enough to hold a CD case upright.
7. Fill the spray bottles with water.

Introduce the Activity

1. Read a book of your choice that reinforces the theme of sprouting plants.
   (**Suggestions**: *A Seed Grows* by Pamela Hickman; *From Seed To Plant* by Gail Gibbons; *The Magic School Bus: Plants Seeds* by Joanna Cole)
2. Introduce the word cards for the unit. Discuss the meaning of new words and concepts.
3. Demonstrate this experiment to the entire class. Follow the steps outlined on the following page.

Seed Sprouter *(cont.)*

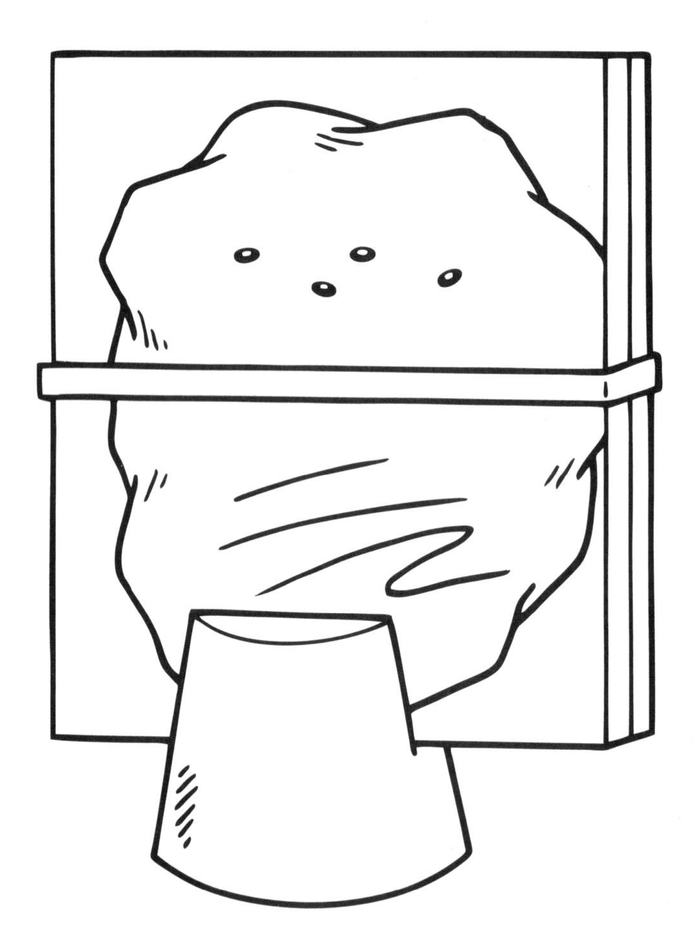

Procedure

1. Print your name on the front of the CD case with a permanent marker.
   Note: Position the CD case so the side that opens is on the bottom.
2. Choose a variety of seeds and observe them with the magnifying lens.
3. Open the CD case. Fold the coffee filter so it fits inside the case.
4. Place the seeds on the coffee filter and spray the seeds with water until the coffee filter is moist.
5. Carefully close the CD case and stand it up on the condiment-cup base. Wrap a rubber band around the seed sprouter to hold it closed.
6. Draw a picture of your seed sprouter in your Mini Book.
7. Place your seed sprouter in a sunny location and observe it closely for one week. Spray your sprouts with water daily. There is a small slit in the top of the CD case that makes this possible without opening the case. Record your observations in your Mini Book. Recordings could be made daily or as schedules permit.
8. Once the seeds have sprouted, use the seedlings to complete the Seedling Activities in the next unit.

Fun Science Questions and Facts

What do seeds need to grow?

Most seeds need soil, water, and light.

Why did some seeds sprout right away and others take longer?

Each seed type has unique characteristics. One of those characteristics is the hardness of the seed coat. Before a seed can sprout, the seed coat needs to be broken. This process varies from seed type to seed type.

What will these sprouts look like when they are fully grown?

If you keep the seed packages, they often have a photo of the fully grown plant.

How long will it take for the sprouts to reproduce the vegetable or fruit that the seeds came from?

It depends on the type of seed. Check the seed packets for the correct information for each seed type. Remember, for many fruit and vegetables to reach maturity, they must be pollinated during the flowering stage.

What will happen to my sprouts if I leave them in the CD case?

They will die because eventually the sprouts will use up all the nutrients within the seed and will need to be transplanted to soil to begin the process of photosynthesis, so it can produce the nutrients that it requires.

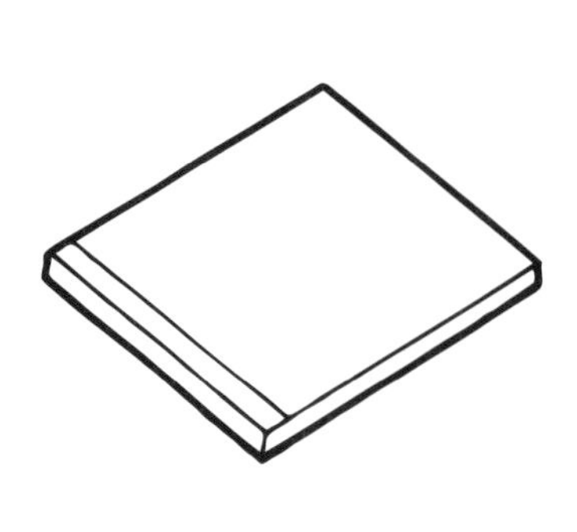

My Seed Sprouter

By: ____________________

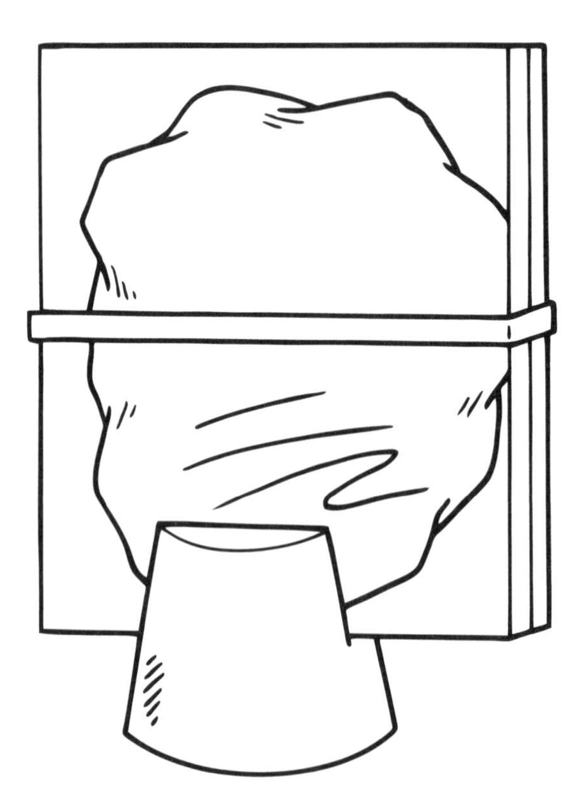

This is what my seed sprouter looks like on Day 1.

This is what my seed sprouter looks like on Day 2.

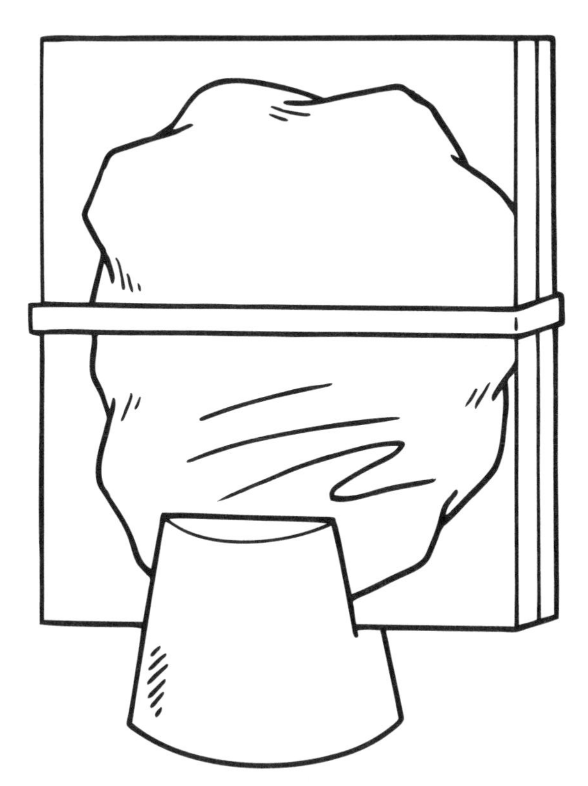

1 This is what my seed sprouter looks like on Day 3.

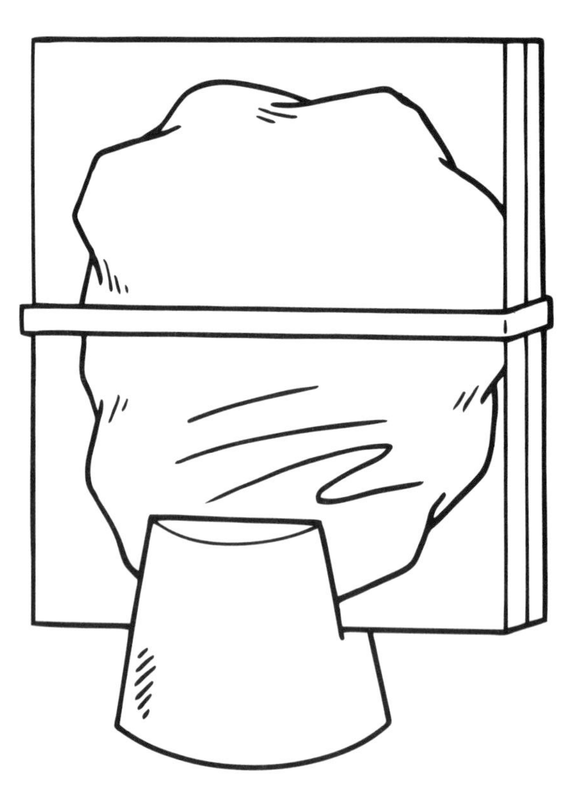

2 This is what my seed sprouter looks like on Day 4.

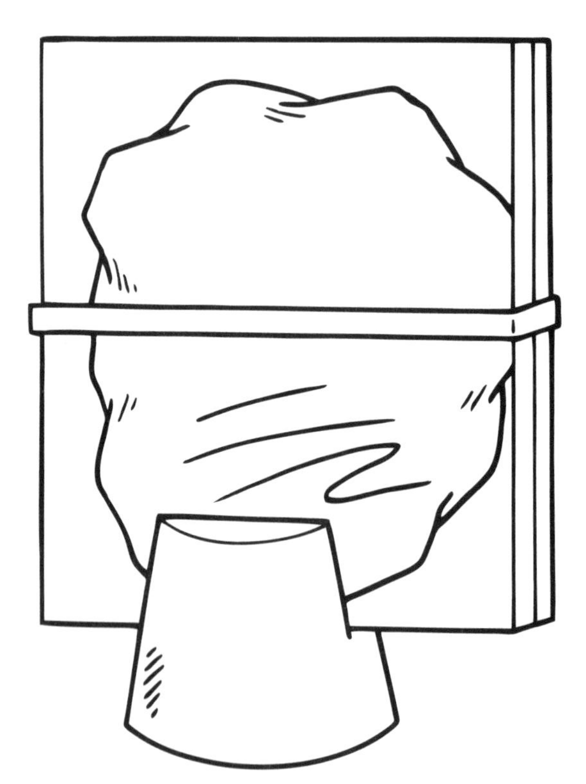

3 This is what my seed sprouter looks like on Day 5.

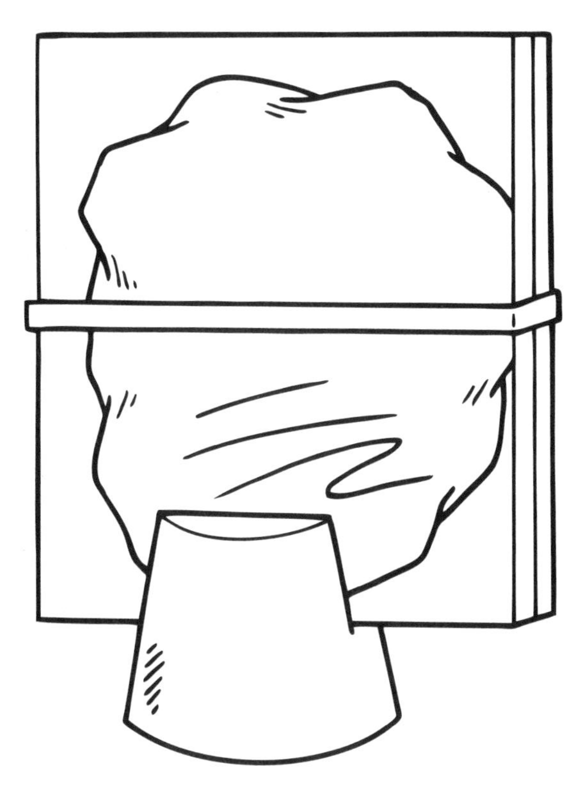

4 This is what my seed sprouter looks like on Day 6.

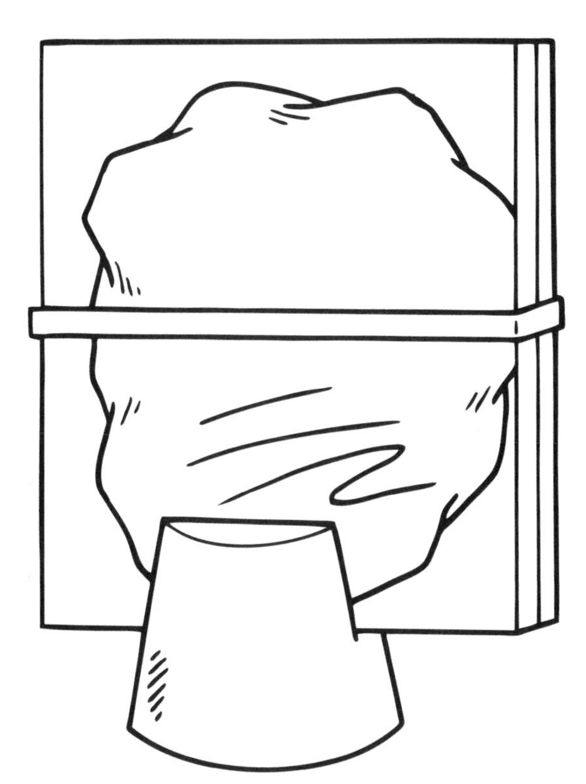

5 This is what my seed sprouter looks like on Day 7.

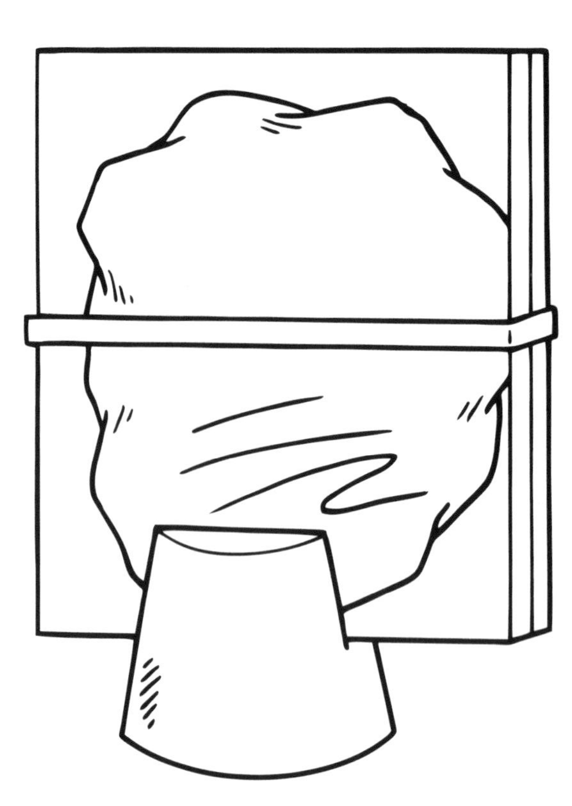

6 This is what my seed sprouter looks like on Day 8.

7 This is what I think my fully grown plant will look like.

Date: ____________________

Dear Parents,

We are planning to study plants in our classroom. In order to complete several of our activities, we are asking for students to bring in any seeds that they would like to share with our class. Each student will also need to bring in a clear, double CD case to use as a seed sprouter.

Please have your student bring in seeds and a double CD case by

________________________ . Thank you.

Date: ____________________

Dear Parents,

We are planning to study plants in our classroom. In order to complete several of our activities, we are asking for students to bring in any seeds that they would like to share with our class. Each student will also need to bring in a clear, double CD case to use as a seed sprouter.

Please have your student bring in seeds and a double CD case by

________________________ . Thank you.

Flower
Seeds

seed

water

light

germinate

sprout

plant

Seedling Activities

Demonstration Materials

- diagram of a seedling (The featured diagram is a kidney bean seed.)
- seedlings
- permanent marker
- ruler
- paper towels
- small pot or cup with 2–3 small holes poked in the bottom
- soil
- water
- magnifying glass
- craft stick
- white glue
- Science Journal—*Seedling Diagram* (page 163)
- Science Journal—*Seedling Illustration* (page 164)
- Science Journal—*Seedling Growth Chart* (page 165)
- Mini Book—*Life Cycle of a Plant* (pages 166–169)
- Ruler—*Seedling Activities* (page 170)
- Word Cards—*Seedling Activities* (page 171)

Student Materials

- seedlings from Seed Sprouter experiment (1 per student)
- permanent markers
- rulers (optional)
- paper towels
- small pots or cups (1 per student)
- soil
- water
- magnifying glass
- white glue
- craft sticks (1 per student)
- Science Journal—*Seedling Diagram* (page 163)
- Science Journal—*Seedling Illustration* (page 164)
- Science Journal—*Seedling Growth Chart* (page 165)
- Mini Book—*Life Cycle of a Plant* (pages 166–169)
- Rulers—*Seedling Activities* (page 170)

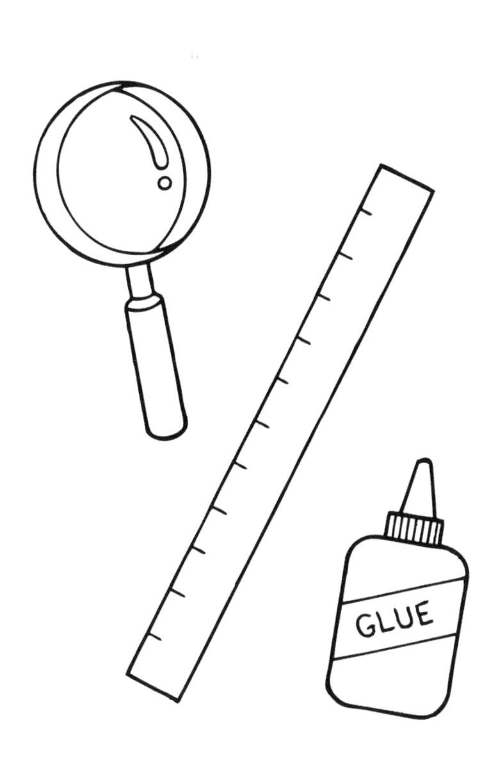

Seedling Activities *(cont.)*

Getting Ready for the Activity

1. Make copies of the Science Journal pages. Give one copy of each to every student.
2. Make copies of the Mini Book. Assemble the books prior to the activity. Give one book to each student.
3. Reproduce word cards on cardstock (or heavy paper), laminate, and display. Reproduce and laminate rulers (page 170).
4. Create a poster-sized diagram of a seedling. Label the main parts. (**Note:** You may wish to research a diagram specific to the seeds your students are planting. The diagram below is for a kidney bean.)

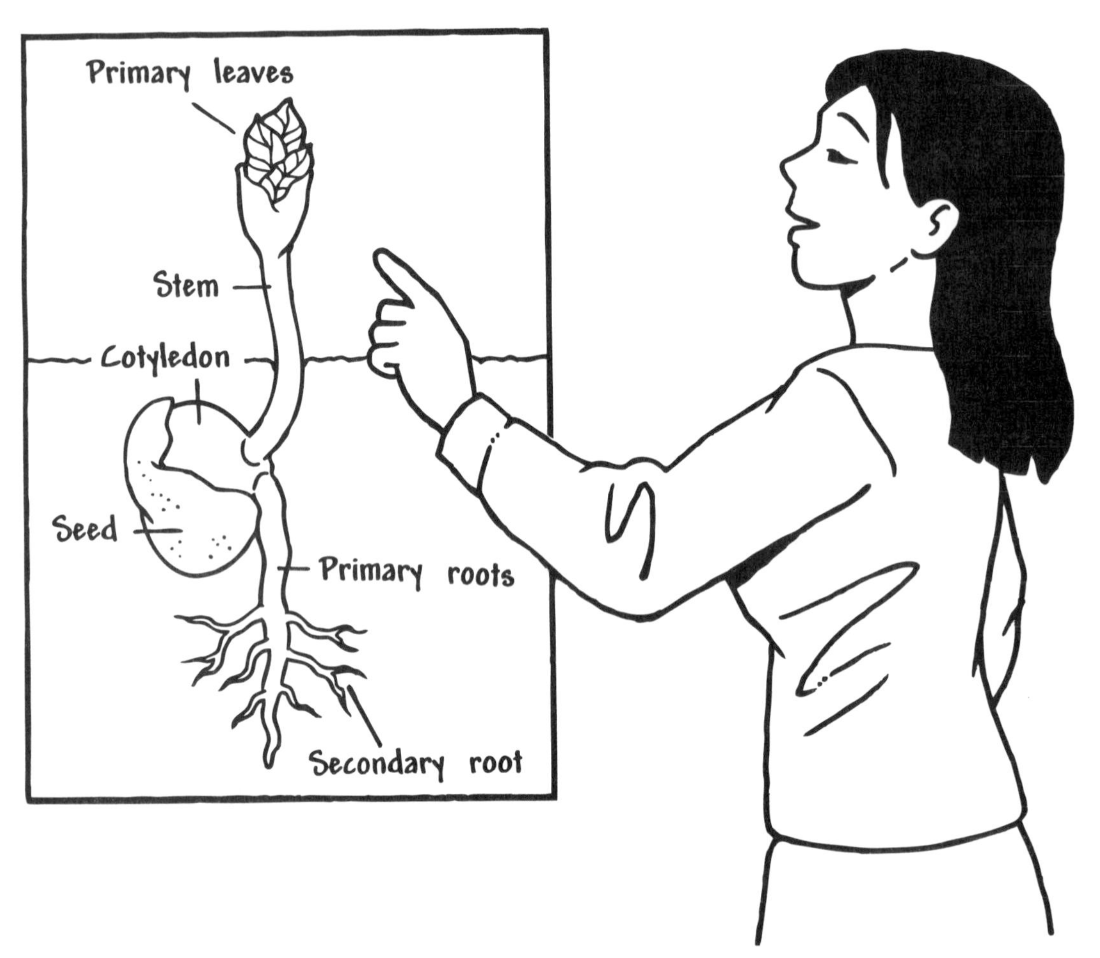

Introduce the Activity

1. Read a book of your choice that reinforces the theme of planting.
   (**Suggestions:** *The Tiny Seed* by Eric Carle; *Tops and Bottoms* by Janet Stevens; *Growing Vegetable Soup* by Lois Ehlert)
2. Use a seedling diagram to identify the parts of the seedling (e.g., seed, primary roots, secondary roots, cotyledon, primary leaves, and stem).
3. Introduce the word cards for the unit. Discuss the meaning of new words and concepts.
4. Demonstrate this experiment to the entire class. Follow the steps outlined on the next page.

Seedling Activities *(cont.)*

Procedure

1. Observe the seedlings in the CD case, the "seed sprouter." Use a magnifying glass to identify the main parts of the seedling.
2. Record your observations on the Science Journal page.
3. Print your name on a small pot or cup and fill it with soil.
4. Add enough water to make the soil damp.
5. Dig a small hole in the soil and gently transfer the seedling from the sprouter to the hole. Cover up the roots with soil.
6. Look closely at the seedling. Record your observations on the Science Journal—*Seedling Illustration.* Draw a picture of what you predict your seedling will look like when it is fully grown.
7. Attach your paper ruler to a craft stick, leaving at least 1" at the bottom of the stick. Place the ruler in the pot with the 0 at soil level.
8. Measure the seedling. Record the result on the Science Journal—*Seedling Growth Chart.* Each day for one week record the height of your seedling.
9. Place your seedling in a sunny location and observe it closely for one week. Spray the seedling with water daily.
10. Complete the Mini Book. Take it home to share with your family.
11. Observe and record the seedling's height for five days on the Science Journal—*Seedling Activities*. Take it home to share with your family.

Fun Science Questions and Facts

What do seeds need to grow?

Most seeds need soil, water, and light.

What makes my seedling lean to one side?

Plants will move toward a light source.

Why are some of my seedlings growing better than others?

Every seed is different, and some are hardier and faster growing than others.

Should I transplant my seedlings again when they get bigger?

In order for your seedlings to continue to grow, they will need to be moved to a larger container with soil or transplanted into the ground. The seed (embryo) contains enough nutrients for the seedling, but to continue to grow, the plant needs to be able to begin the production of its nutrients through photosynthesis. When sunlight shines on the chlorophyll in a leaf, the chlorophyll will mix with water from the ground and carbon dioxide from the air to make food for the plant. A byproduct of this production of food is oxygen, which is sent into the air through its leaves. The seedlings will need soil, sunlight, and water to sustain themselves.

Name ____

Seedling Diagram

This is a diagram of my seedling growing in the ground.

Use the words below to label plant parts.

Word Bank

roots seed leaves stem

Name ____

Seedling Illustration

I chose one seedling to measure. On the day that I transplanted my seedling, it was ______ inches tall. It looked like this.	This is what I predict my seedling will look like when it is fully grown.

Name ____

Seedling Growth Chart

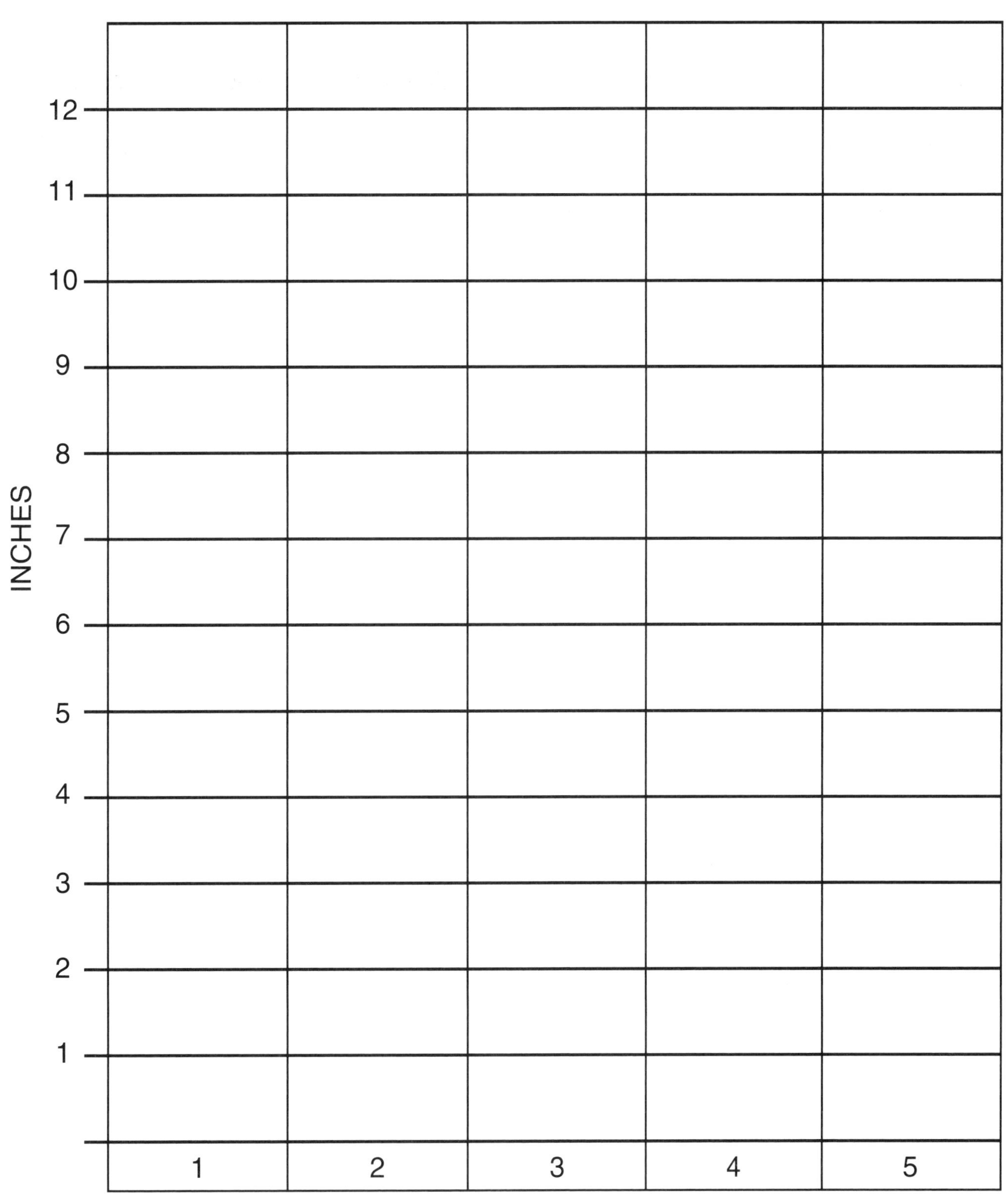

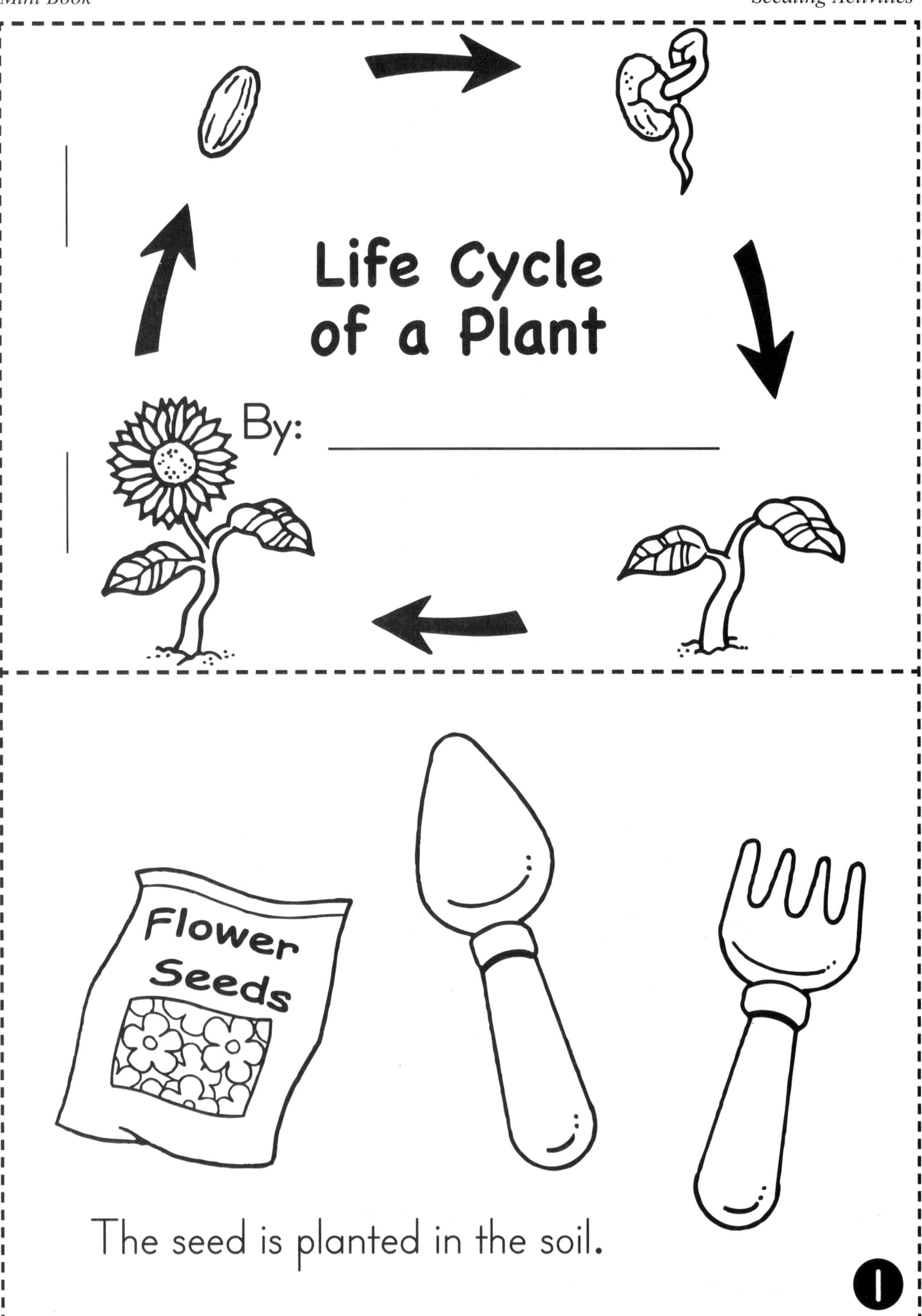
Life Cycle of a Plant
By: ______________________
Flower Seeds
The seed is planted in the soil.
1

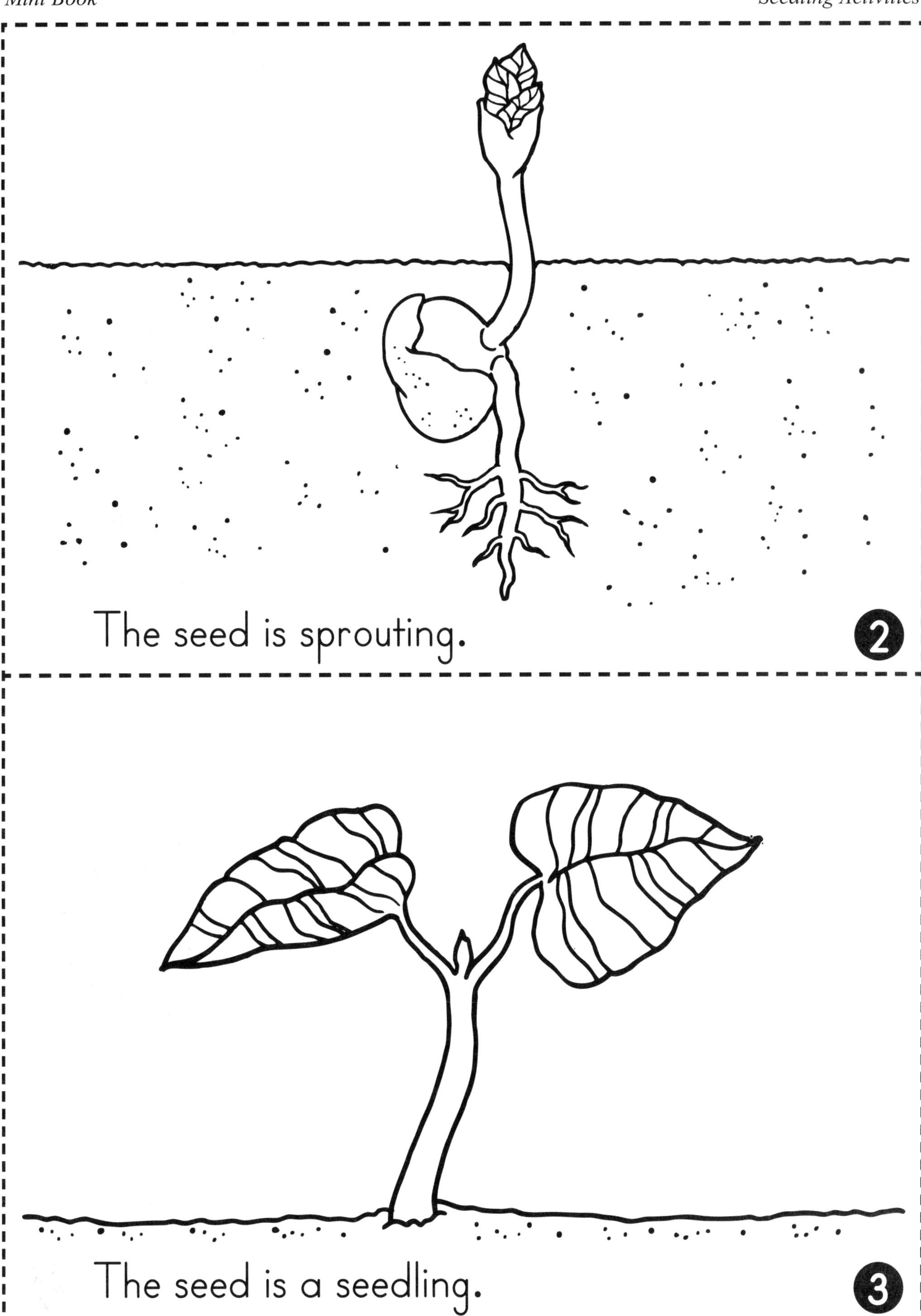
The seed is sprouting.
2
The seed is a seedling.
3

The seedling grows into a plant.

The plant flowers and produces more seeds. 5

The seeds will grow into plants.

6

The life cycle of a seed goes on and on.

7

in. 1 2 3 4 5 6 7

in. 1 2 3 4 5 6 7

in. 1 2 3 4 5 6 7

in. 1 2 3 4 5 6 7

in. 1 2 3 4 5 6 7

in. 1 2 3 4 5 6 7

in. 1 2 3 4 5 6 7

in. 1 2 3 4 5 6 7

seed

cotyledon

primary leaves

primary roots

secondary roots

stem

Seed Travel

Demonstration Materials

- various types of seeds (e.g., marigold flowers, bean pods, peach, cherry, carrot, sunflower, mulberry tree, sycamore tree, etc.)
- dishpan-size tub filled with water
- towel
- 2 containers (one labeled "wet" and one labeled "dry")
- small, furry stuffed animal
- pencils, colored pencils, and crayons
- index cards
- small fan (optional for flyer experiment)
- Science Journal—*Seed Travel* (page 176)
- Word Cards—*Seed Travel* (page 178)
- Station Cards—*Seed Travel* (page 179)

Student Materials

- various types of seeds (e.g., beans, marigold flower seeds, bean pods, peach, cherry, carrot, sunflower, mulberry tree, sycamore tree, etc.)
- pencils, colored pencils, and crayons
- index cards
- Science Journal—*Seed Travel* (page 176)
- Family Connection—*Seed Travel* (page 177)

Getting Ready for the Activity

1. Make copies of the Science Journal page. Give two copies to each student.
2. Make copies of the Family Connection page. Give one copy to each student.
3. Reproduce word cards on cardstock (or heavy paper), laminate, and display.
4. Print the names of the seed types on index cards and laminate.
5. Prepare the following stations prior to student participation. Determine how and when students will rotate (plan on 10 minutes per station).

Flyer Station: various seeds, seed cards, pencils, fan (optional), and Station Card

Hitchhiker Station: small, furry stuffed animals, various seeds, seed cards, pencils, and Station Card

Floater Station: tub filled halfway with water, towel, various seeds, seed cards, pencils, container for wet seeds, and Station Card

Seed Travel *(cont.)*

Introduce the Activity

1. Read a book of your choice that reinforces the theme of seed travel. (**Suggestions:** *All About Seeds* by Melvin Berger; *How and Why Seeds Travel* by Elaine Pascoe; *How Seeds Travel* by Cynthia Overbeck)
2. Introduce the word cards for the unit. Discuss the meaning of new words and concepts.
3. Review the various seed types.
4. Explain that the class will divide up into groups and participate in three separate seed-travel experiments. Each student will conduct his or her own experiments using the materials provided at each station.
5. Describe the procedure for each of the experiments before having students form groups.

Procedure

Flyer Station: Is the seed a flyer?

1. Choose a seed and find the matching seed card. Record the name of the seed on your Science Journal page.
2. Predict if you think the seed will be a flyer. Will it fly through the air when blown off of your hand? Or, will it drop straight down to the ground? Share your prediction with another person in the group.
3. Take the seed and place it on your flattened palm. Either move your hand slowly in front of the fan or blow the seed off of your hand.
4. Observe whether or not the seed flies. Record your observations on the Science Journal page.
5. Repeat this procedure for at least two additional types of seeds and record your observations.

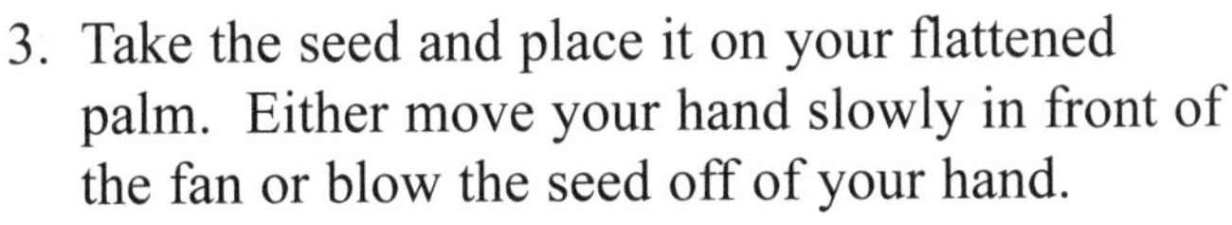

Seed Travel *(cont.)*

Procedure *(cont.)*

Hitchhiker Station: Is the seed a hitchhiker?

1. Choose a seed and find the matching seed card. Record the name of the seed on your Science Journal page.
2. Predict if you think the seed will be a hitchhiker. Will the seed attach itself to the animal? Tell a member of your group your prediction.
3. Take the seed and place it on the table. Choose a stuffed animal and pretend to walk it over your seed.
4. Observe whether or not the seed becomes a hitchhiker when the stuffed animal touches it. Did the seed stick to the animal? Record your observations on your Science Journal page.
5. Repeat this procedure for at least two additional types of seeds and record your observations.

Floater Station: Is the seed a floater?

1. Choose a seed and find the matching seed card. Record the name of the seed on your Science Journal page.
2. Predict if you think the seed will be a floater. Tell a member of your group your prediction.
3. Take the seed and place it carefully in the tub of water on the table.
4. Observe whether or not the seed floats in the water. Record your observations on the Science Journal page.
5. Remove the seed from the tub and place it in a container for wet seeds, which should be separate from the dry seeds.
6. Repeat this procedure for at least two additional types of seeds and record your observations.

Sunflower Seeds

Family Connection

Send home the Family Connection page and ask students to complete it with their families.

Fun Science Questions and Facts

Which types of seeds were hitchhikers? Floaters? Flyers?

It seems lots of tree seeds were flyers. Weeds were hitchhikers, and the larger seeds were often floaters.

What types of seeds were the easiest to predict how they traveled?

Some seeds have easily recognizable wing-type shapes that let you know they are flyers, and some have stickers to let you know they are hitchhikers. It's harder to tell just by observation whether or not a seed will be a floater.

Are there any other ways that seeds travel?

Yes, animals that eat fruit with seeds also help to transport seeds. The animals digest the fruit but not the seeds, which come out of their bodies in their droppings.

Have you ever transported a seed?

Stickers can be seeds and they may be transported on your clothing from place to place. When you eat fruit and throw the seeds on the ground, you are transporting seeds.

Which animals do you think help transport seeds?

Seeds are transported by birds, bats, and other animals that eat fruit from trees. Rodents and small mammals move seeds from place to place as they store them in their burrows and nests for the winter months.

Name ____

Seed Travel

SEED AND DRAWING	FLOATER (yes or no)	HITCHHIKER (yes or no)	FLYER (yes or no)
Sunflower Seeds	YES	NO	NO

Name ____

Home School Connection

We have been conducting experiments to determine how seeds travel.

Your child's assignment is to demonstrate and explain some of the experiments that we conducted in class.

Spend some time talking to your child about these questions.

- What does it mean if a seed is a flyer? floater? hitchhiker?
- Why do seeds travel in different ways?
- What types of seeds do you have around your home?

Please assist your child in filling up a small bowl with water and finding a small furry stuffed animal. You may also use a towel, if a stuffed animal is not available.

Complete the seed travel experiments using the attached seed or seeds of your choice. Make a *prediction* before the experiment, *perform* the experiment, and then *record* your observations on the chart and answer the questions below.

Seed Travel Experiments

SEED	FLYER	FLOATER	HITCHHIKER
Foxtail	no	no	yes

1. What is a characteristic of a *flyer*? ____________________________

2. What is a characteristic of a *floater*? ____________________________

3. What is a characteristic of a *hitchhiker*? ____________________________

seed

flyer

floater

hitchhiker

yes

no

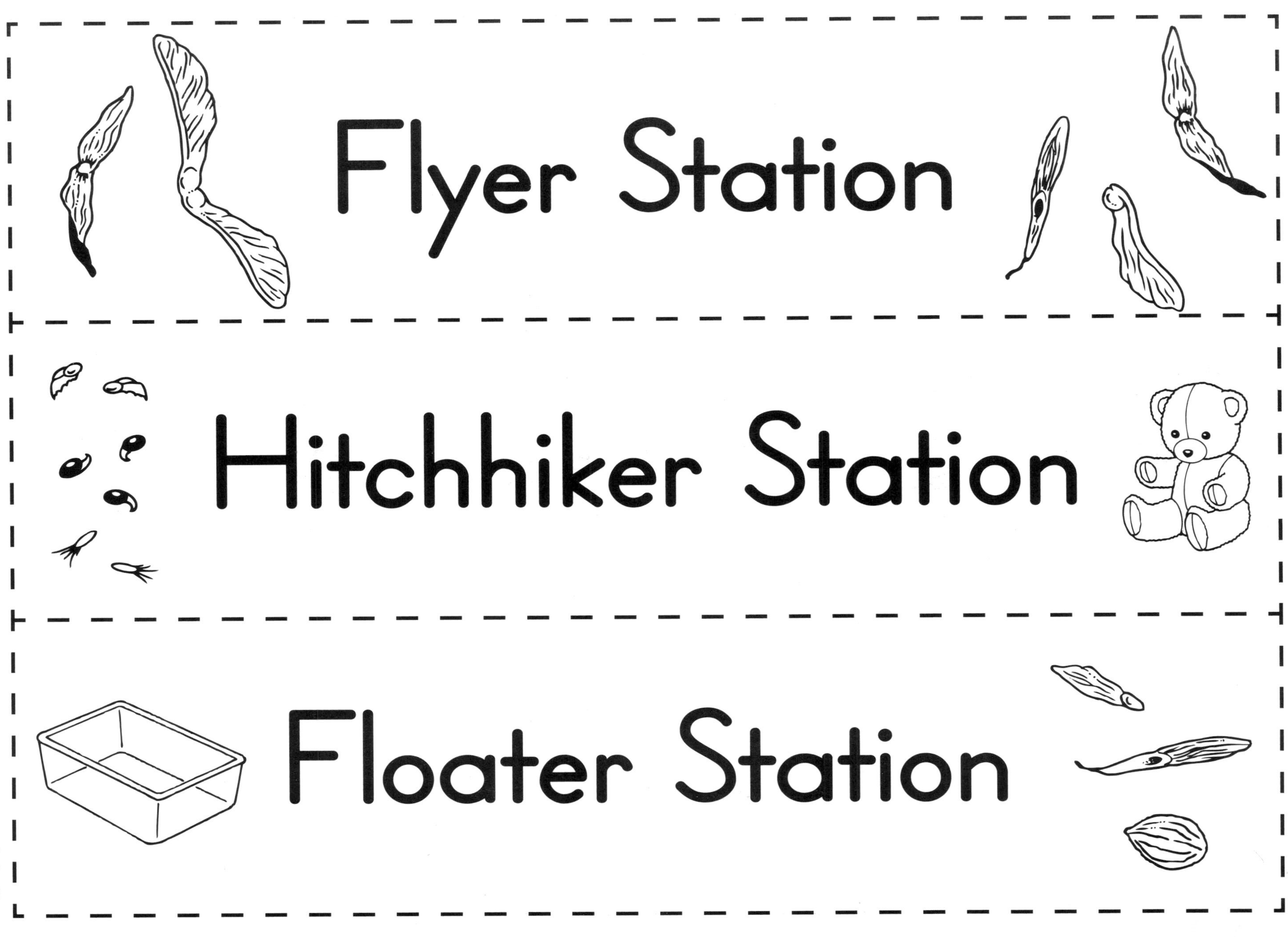

Flyer Station
Hitchhiker Station
Floater Station

Butterfly Symmetry

Demonstration Materials

- white construction paper or card stock (9" x 12")
- fabric paint with dropper top or tempera paint in squeeze bottles (variety of colors)
- newspaper or other paper to cover the work space
- pencil
- scissors
- tag board pattern of *Butterfly Wing Pattern* (page 184)
- Science Journal—*Butterfly Symmetry Observation* (page 185)
- Word Cards—*Butterfly Symmetry* (pages 188–189)

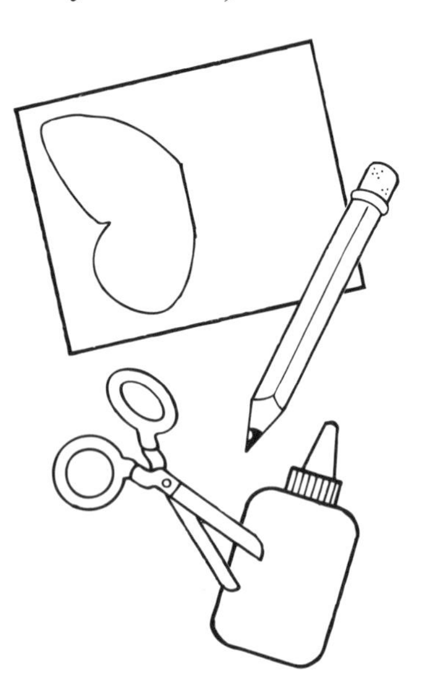

Student Materials

- white construction paper or card stock (9" x 12") (1 per student)
- fabric paint with dropper top or tempera paint in squeeze bottles (variety of colors)
- newspaper or other paper to cover the work space
- pencils
- scissors
- Butterfly Wing Pattern (1 for every 2–3 students)
- Science Journal—*Butterfly Symmetry Observation* (page 185)
- Science Journal—*Symmetry Fun* (page 186)
- Family Connection—*Butterfly Symmetry* (page 187)

Getting Ready for the Activity

1. Make copies of the Science Journal pages. Give one copy of each sheet/page to each student.
2. Make copies of the Family Connection page. Give one copy to each student.
3. Reproduce word cards on cardstock (or heavy paper), laminate, and display.
4. Prepare the workstations prior to student participation. Determine how and when students will rotate (plan on 15 minutes per station).
5. Use the newspaper to cover the table in the paint station.
6. Set up a hand-washing station.
7. Trace and cut out one tagboard *Butterfly Wing Pattern* for every 2–3 students.

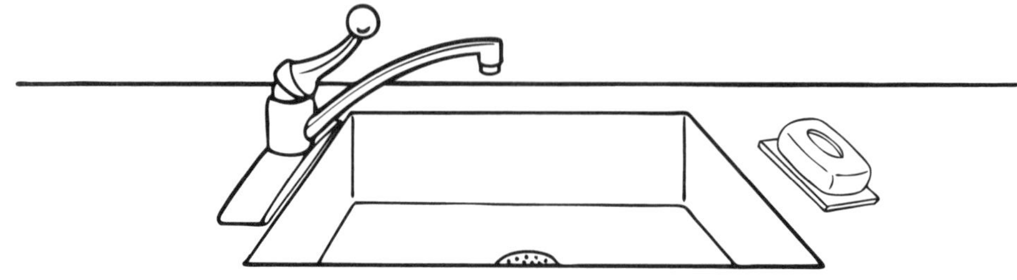

Butterfly Symmetry *(cont.)*

Introduce the Activity

1. Read a book of your choice that reinforces the topic of butterflies. (**Suggestions:** *Where Butterflies Grow* by Joanne Ryder; *Butterflies Fly* by Yvonne Winer)
2. Introduce the word cards for the unit. Discuss the meaning of new words and concepts.
3. Explain that the class will divide up into three groups and participate in three separate observation experiments. Each student will complete the experiments using the materials present at each station.
4. Describe the procedure for each of the experiments before having students break off into the three groups.

Note: Teachers might want to have all students trace and cut out their butterflies. As they finish, call them over one group at a time to paint. Ask the rest of the class to complete the Science Journal page—*Symmetry Fun* while they wait for their turn to paint.

Procedure

Tracing and Cutting Station

1. Fold the piece of white paper in half.
2. Place the *Butterfly Wing Pattern* with the straight edge on the folded side of the paper. Trace the butterfly wing.
3. Cut on the line but do not cut along the fold. Unfold your butterfly.
4. Print your name on the back of the butterfly.

Butterfly Symmetry *(cont.)*

Procedure *(cont.)*

Painting Station

1. Fold your butterfly in half with your name on the inside.
2. Apply drops of different colors of paint on the butterfly wing.
3. Lift the painted wing and unfold it. Lay it flat.
4. Gently fold the side without paint over on top of the side with the paint drops.
5. Use your fingers to carefully rub the top of the folded butterfly to spread out the paint inside the wings. Some paint will ooze out of the edges onto the newspaper.
6. When the paint has been smoothed out, carefully unfold the butterfly wings and admire your beautiful butterfly with symmetrical wings.
7. Place on a flat surface to dry.
8. When dry, attach to a piece of paper and draw three body parts, six legs, and two antennae.

Observation and Recording Station

1. Observe your butterfly when it is dry. Record your observations on your Science Journal—*Butterfly Symmetry Observation* page.

Family Connection

Send home the Family Connection page and ask students to complete it with their families.

Fun Science Questions and Facts

What does *symmetry* mean?

When something is exactly the same on either side of an axis (a straight line). If you draw a line down the middle of an object and both sides are exactly the same, it is symmetrical.

Are all butterflies symmetrical?

Yes, they all have a vertical line of symmetry right down the middle of their three main body parts.

What else can you think of that is symmetrical?

Quilts, people, other animals, etc.

How many body parts does a butterfly have?

A butterfly has three body parts—head, thorax, and abdomen.

How are butterflies and moths the same?

They are the same in the following ways:

- Both have wings and fly
- Both have three main body parts
- Both lay eggs
- Both are insects
- Both have many different colors
- Both are symmetrical
- Both go through metamorphosis (stages include *egg, larva, pupae, and adult*)

How are butterflies and moths different?

BUTTERFLY	MOTH
Diurnal (active in the day)	Nocturnal (active at night)
Rests with wings open	Rests with wings closed
Has straight antennae with a knob	Most have feathery antennae

Butterfly Wing Pattern

Copy onto cardstock or trace onto tagboard.

Name ____

Butterfly Symmetry Observation

Observe your butterfly and record what it looks like.

Name ____

Symmetry Fun

Instructions: Look at the different pictures in the boxes below. Color the objects that are symmetrical. Remember that both sides need to be exactly the same. Put an X on objects that are asymmetrical (not symmetrical).

Name____

Home School Connection

We have been discussing symmetry in class. Please have your child explain what symmetry means. Then, have him or her color in the butterfly symmetrically.

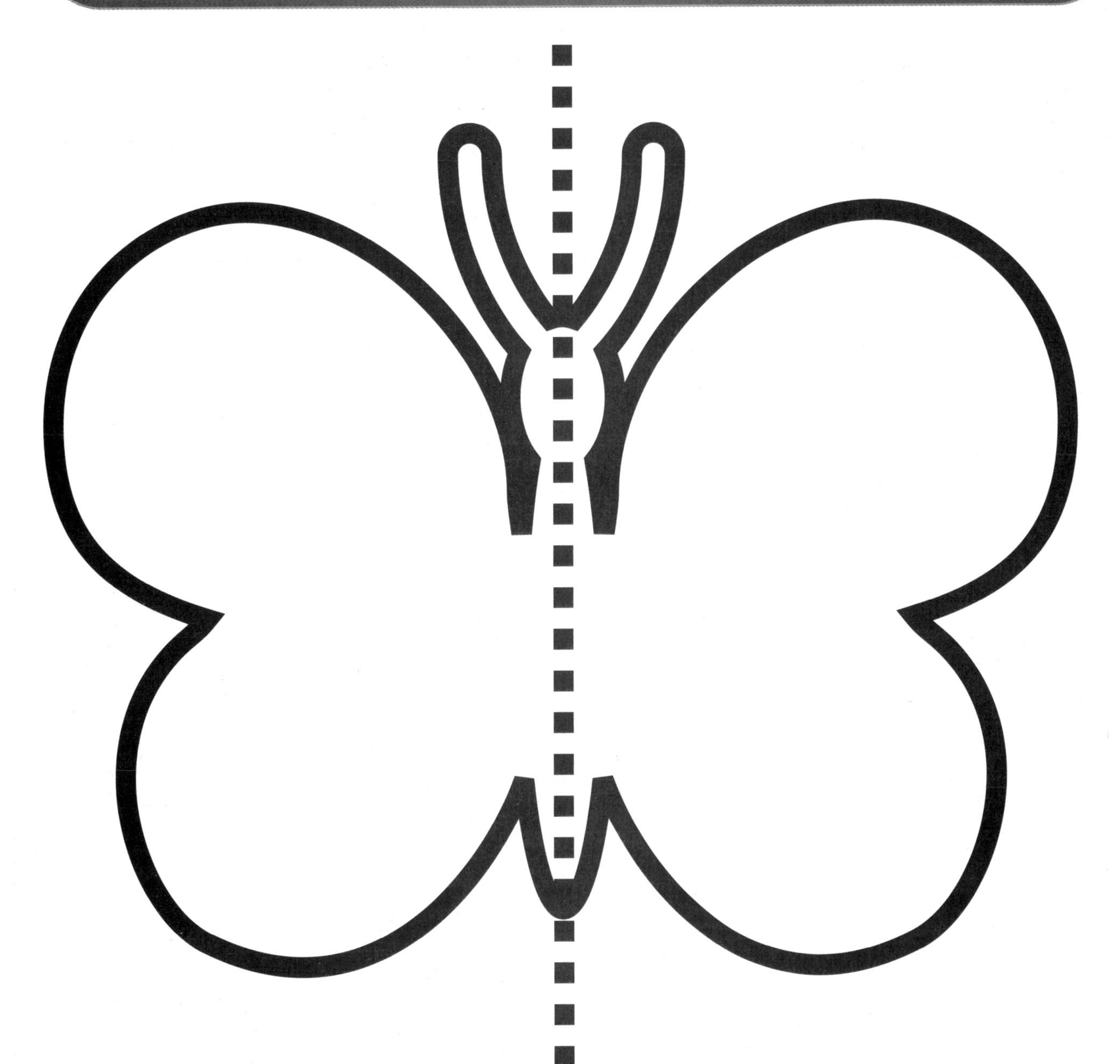

Remember: Both sides need to be identical for it to be symmetrical.

butterfly

wing

head

thorax

abdomen

legs

insect

antennae

moth

same

different

symmetry

Frog Life Cycle

Demonstration Materials

- sentence strip (to create a "crown")
- glue
- crayons, markers, and pencils
- scissors
- hole punches
- stapler
- Science Journal—*Frog Life Cycle Observation* (page 193)
- Cutouts—*Life Cycle of a Frog* (page 194)
- Word Cards—*Frog Life Cycle* (page 196)

TOADS	FROGS
Nocturnal (active during the _______________)	Diurnal (active during the day)
_______________ skin	Smooth skin
Usually walk	Usually _______________
Back and front legs are similar length	Back legs are longer than _______________ legs
Live alone	Live in_______________
Can live away from _______________	Prefer to live near water
Lay _______________ in strings	Lay eggs in clumps

Student Materials

- sentence strip (1 per student)
- glue stick (1 per student)
- crayons, markers, and pencils
- scissors (1 per student)
- hole punches (1 per group)
- stapler (1 per group)
- Science Journal—*Frog Life Cycle Observation* (page 193)
- Cut-outs—*Life Cycle of a Frog* (page 194)
- Family Connection—*Frog and Toad Comparison* (page 195)

Getting Ready for the Activity

1. Make copies of the Science Journal pages. Give one copy of each page to every student.
2. Make copies of the Family Connection page. Give one copy to each student.
3. Reproduce word cards on cardstock (or heavy paper), laminate, and display. Have an example of the life cycle crown already completed.
4. Prepare the workstations prior to student participation.

Frog Life Cycle *(cont.)*

Introduce the Activity

1. Read a book of your choice about the life cycle of a frog. (**Suggestions:** *Frogs* by Gail Gibbons; *Tale of a Tadpole* by Barbara Ann Porte; *What is an Amphibian* by Bobbie Kalman)
2. Introduce the word cards for the unit. Discuss the meaning of new words and concepts.
3. Demonstrate this experiment to the entire class. Follow the steps outlined below.

Procedure

1. Add details to the frogs on your Science Journal page. Cut out the frogs. Use a hole punch to punch out some eggs from the scrap paper.
2. Take a sentence strip and put it around your forehead. Have someone make a vertical mark across the strip to indicate the circumference of your head. This will show you what part of the strip will be visible when it is stapled to make a crown.
3. Place the cutouts on the sentence strip in the following order: eggs, tadpole, froglet with back legs, froglet with front and back legs, frog (with no tail and both sets of legs). Once they have been positioned correctly, glue them onto the sentence strip.
4. Label each stage of development on your life cycle crown.
5. Staple the crown at the vertical line.
6. Pair up and explain the life cycle to your partner.
7. Complete the Science Journal page.

Family Connection

Send home the Family Connection page and ask students to complete it with their families.

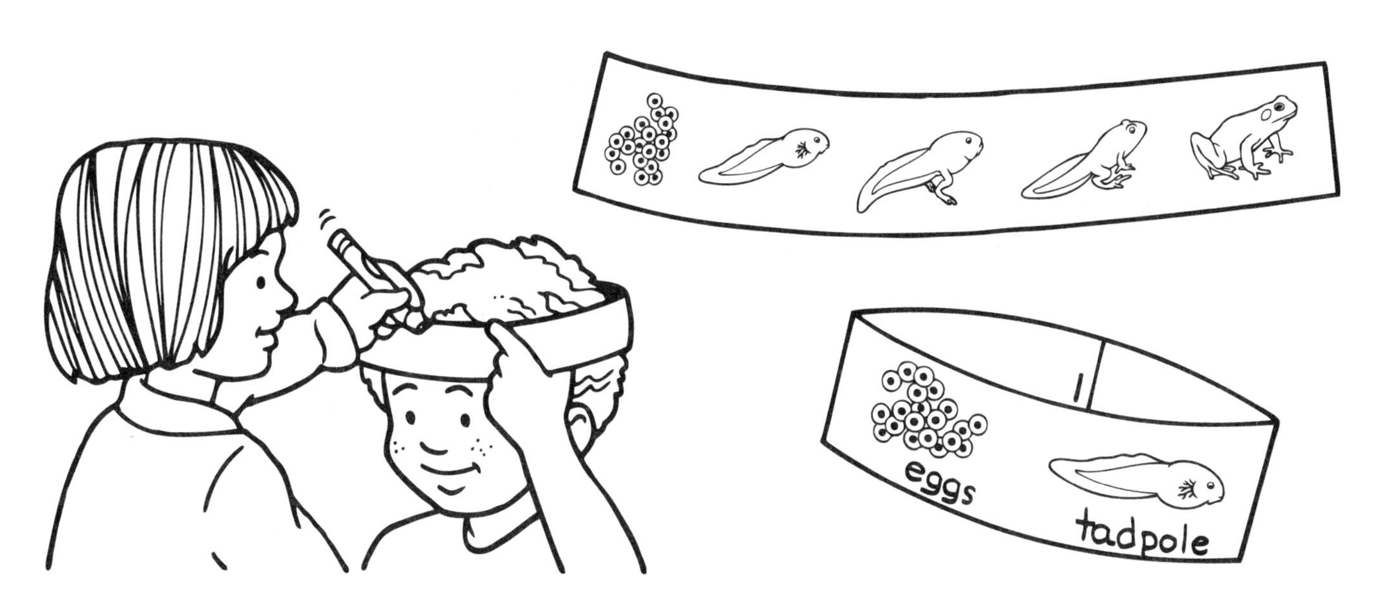

Fun Science Questions and Facts

What is the name of a scientist who studies frogs?

The scientist is a herpetologist.

How long does it take for a tadpole to turn into a frog?

Most froglets make the move onto land at around 16 weeks old. However, most will be almost one year old before they are fully grown and able to reproduce. There are some species that take many years to be fully grown and reproduce.

What type of animal is a frog?

It is an amphibian.

What are other examples of amphibians?

Other examples are toads, salamanders, and newts.

Do frogs have teeth?

Yes, they have teeth in their upper jaw.

Is a toad the same as a frog?

They are the same in the following ways:

- Both are amphibians
- Both breathe through gills as babies and lungs as adults
- Both lay eggs
- Both have skin as a body covering
- Both are cold-blooded
- Both have similar life cycles
- Both have species that are poisonous

Here are some differences between toads and frogs.

TOADS	FROGS
Nocturnal (active at night)	Diurnal (active during the day)
Bumpy skin	Smooth skin
Usually walk	Usually hop
Back and front legs are similar length	Back legs are longer than front
Live alone	Live in groups
Can live away from water	Prefers to live near water
Lay eggs in strings	Lay eggs in clumps
Toothless	Have teeth in upper jaw

Name______________________________

Frog Life Cycle Observation

Fill in the chart to show the life cycle of a frog.

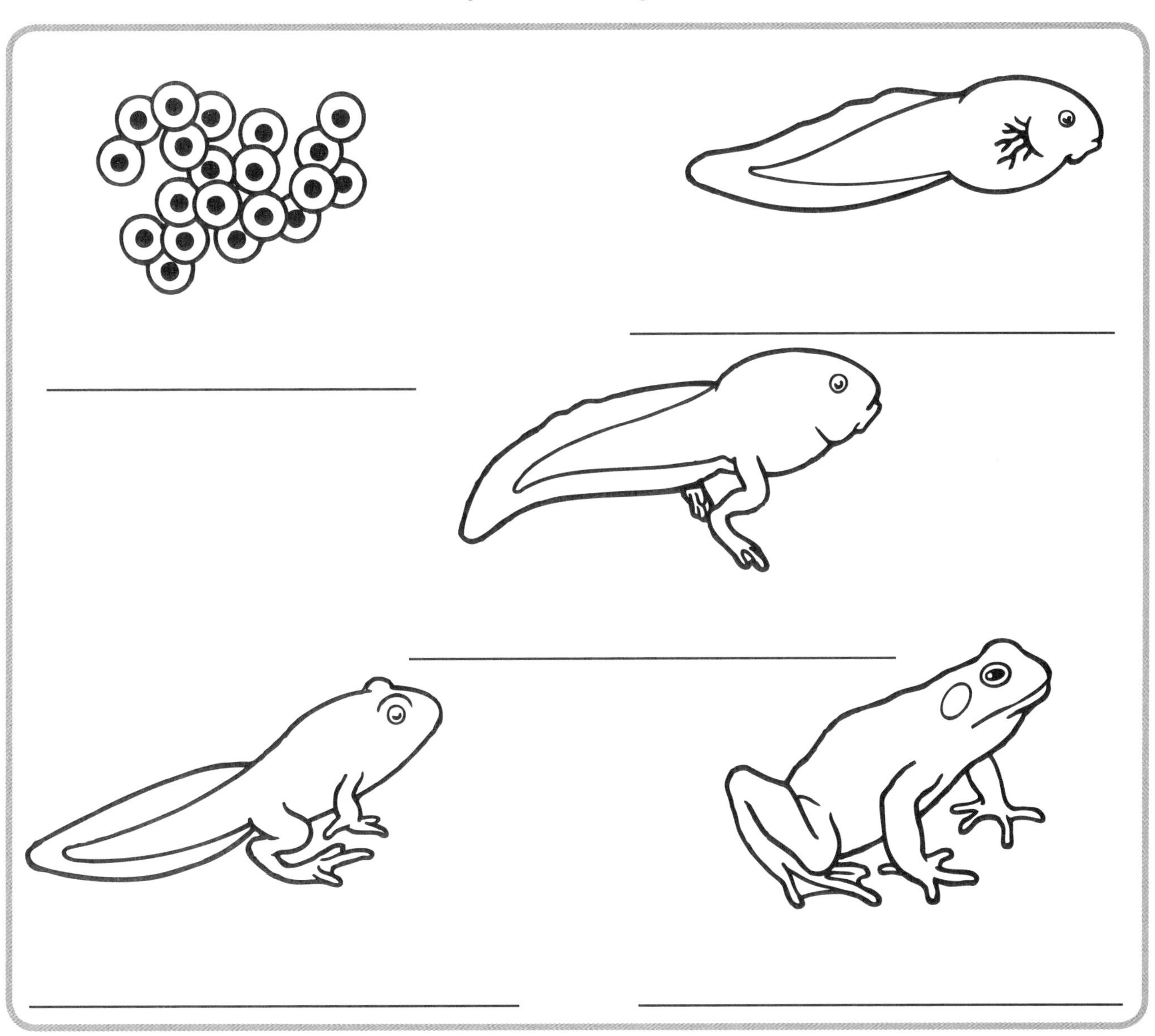

Word Bank

eggs	tadpole	frog
froglet with back and front legs	froglet with back legs	

Life Cycle of the Frog

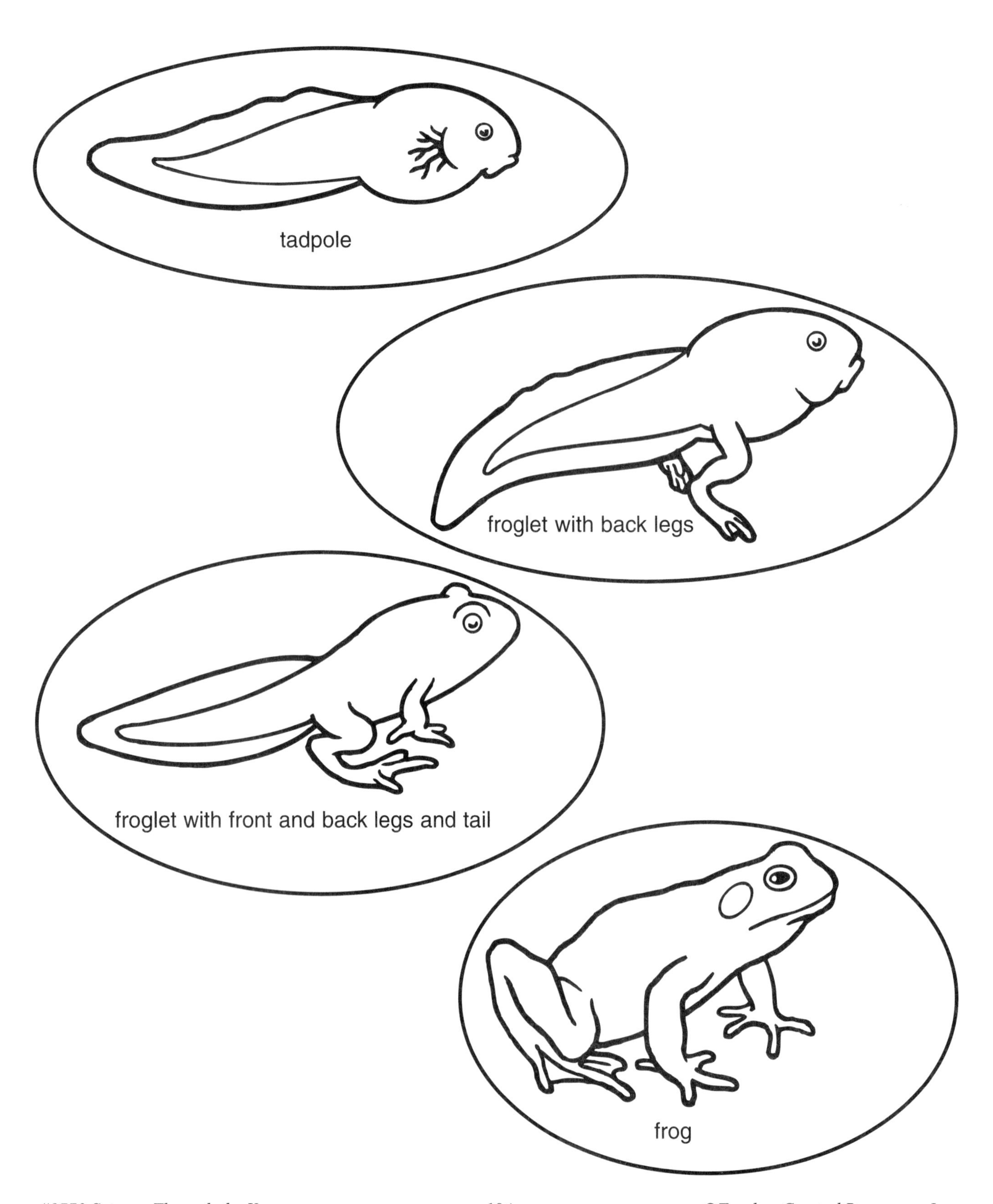

Name ____

Home School Connection

We have been studying frogs and toads in class. Please have your child explain some of the differences and similarities between these two types of amphibians.

Work with your child to complete the following chart using the words from the word bank below.

TOADS	FROGS
Nocturnal (active during the ______________)	Diurnal (active during the day)
______________ skin	Smooth skin
Usually walk	Usually ______________
Back and front legs are similar length	Back legs are longer than ______________ legs
Live alone	Live in______________
Can live away from ______________	Prefer to live near water
Lay ______________ in strings	Lay eggs in clumps

Word Bank

bumpy, eggs, hop, groups, night, front, water

tadpole

eggs

froglet with back legs

froglet with front legs

frog

life cycle

Soda Surprise

Demonstration Materials

- 2-liter bottle of soda
- 20 ounce bottle of soda
- 2 rolls of regular-flavor mentos® mints
- 3–4 index cards
- Science Journal—*Soda Surprise* (page 200)
- Word Cards—*Soda Surprise* (page 201)

Student Materials

- crayons and pencils
- Science Journal—*Soda Surprise* (page 200)

Getting Ready for the Activity

1. Make copies of the Science Journal page. Give one copy to each student.
2. Reproduce word cards on cardstock (or heavy paper), laminate, and display.
3. Find a level workstation outside to conduct this experiment (e.g., grass field, parking lot, etc.) Students will need to be at least six feet away from the activity.
4. Leave the bottles of soda in the refrigerator until just prior to the experiment. The colder the soda, the better the reaction.

Introduce the Activity

1. Read a book of your choice that reinforces the topic of geysers, volcanoes, etc.
   (**Suggestion**: *Volcano: Jump Into Science* by Ellen Prager)
2. Introduce the word cards for the unit. Discuss the meaning of new words and concepts.
3. Demonstrate this experiment to the entire class. Follow the steps outlined on the next page.

Soda Surprise *(cont.)*

Procedure

1. Go outside to the designated area for the experiment.
2. Set the bottles of soda a few feet apart from each other. The students should stand at least six feet away from the soda bottles. Carefully remove the lids from the bottles of soda.
3. Roll up the index card and make a tube. (Taping it shut will make it easier for students to complete this part.) Place six mints in the tube. Model how to hold the mints inside the tube with an index card on the bottom of the tube. Move near the small soda bottle and place the tube over the top of the bottle with the index card between the mints and the neck of the bottle.
4. Count down from five. Pull out the index card and let all the mints drop into the soda bottle. Move back quickly. The reaction is instant and awesome!
5. Repeat the experiment, using 10–12 mints this time and the large, 2-liter bottle of soda. Model how to hold the mints inside of the tube with an index card on the bottom of the tube.
6. Predict what is going to happen this time. Will there be a bigger reaction than last time?
7. Hand the roll of mints to a volunteer, with the instructions to wait until the count down to 0 to let the mints fall into the soda. Have the students count down from five to zero. Pull out the index card and let all the mints drop into the soda bottle. (The volunteer should also be told to move back quickly.)
8. Discuss what was observed when the mints were dropped into the soda. Put the bottles in the recycle bin and go back into the classroom.
9. Record observations on the Science Journal page.

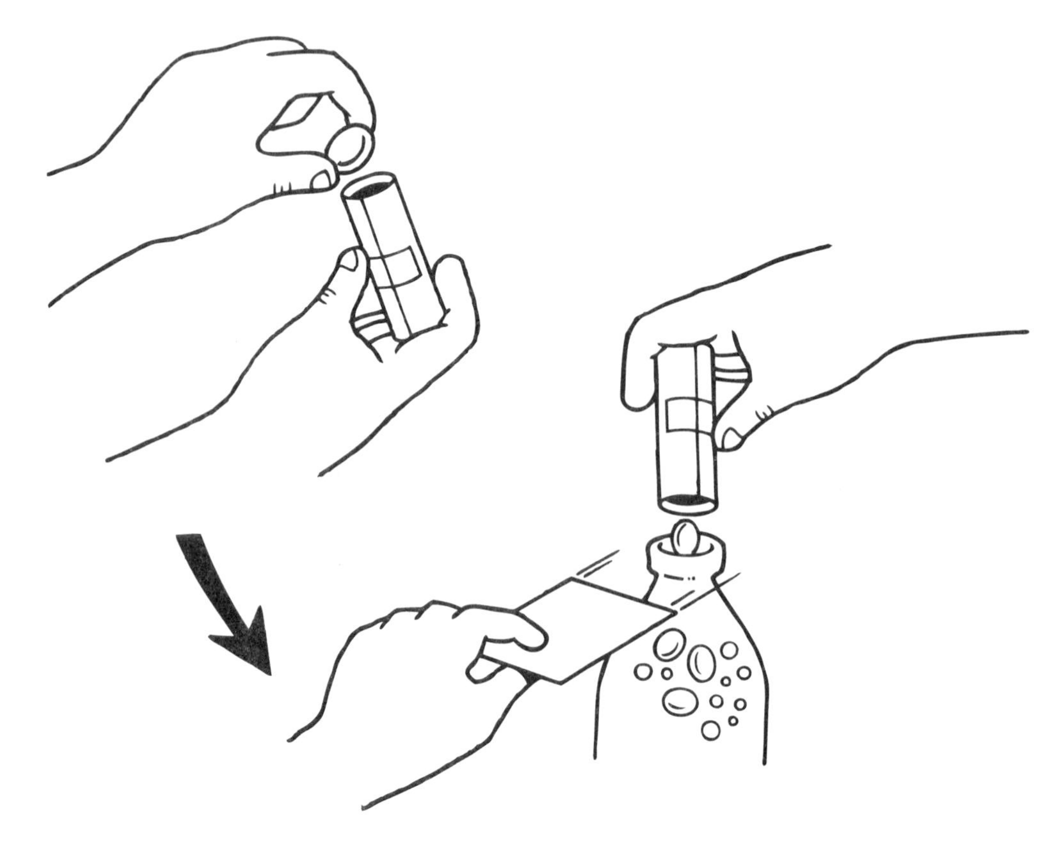

Fun Science Questions and Facts

Why does the soda erupt out of the bottle when the mints are added?

As the mint dissolves in the soda, little pits are created in the outside shell of the mint, and gas (carbon dioxide) bubbles cling to those pits. As the gas is released when the bubbles rise to the surface, it shoots the mints and soda out of the bottle.

Will other candies work?

That would be a good experiment! Wintergreen lifesavers have also been used successfully.

Does it matter what type of soda is used?

There are slight variations in the reaction depending on the type of soda. Diet cola seems to be among the best, but all carbonated sodas will work.

Could this experiment be performed inside?

Actually, it can but you would need to take some precautions. Be sure the ceiling is not lower than 10 feet and that you are not under a light fixture. Set a tablecloth on the ground, next set a large tub in the middle, and set the bottle of soda in the tub. The soda will travel straight up and come straight down, so as long as nothing gets in its way (a ceiling), it works fine indoors.

Extension

Go to *www.eepybird.com* to watch videos and learn more about these activities.

Name______________________________

Soda Surprise

Draw pictures of what you observed when the mints were added to the soda bottles.

How many mints were added?

How many mints were added?

soda

erupt

gas

tube

large

small

Reduce, Reuse, Recycle, Redecorate

Demonstration Materials

- cornstarch packing peanuts (You can tell if they are cornstarch if they dissolve when put into water.)
- cup of water
- damp sponge
- plate
- pencil and crayons
- Science Journal—*Reduce, Reuse, Recycle, Redecorate* (page 205)
- Word Cards—*Reduce, Reuse, Recycle, Redecorate* (page 207)

Student Materials

- cornstarch packing peanuts
- damp sponge (1 per workstation)
- plate (1 per workstation)
- pencils and crayons
- Science Journal—*Reduce, Reuse, Recycle, Redecorate* (page 205)
- Family Connection—*Reduce, Reuse, Recycle, Redecorate* (page 206)

Getting Ready for the Activity

1. Make copies of the Science Journal page. Give one copy to each student.
2. Make copies of the Family Connection page. Give one copy to each student.
3. Reproduce word cards on cardstock (or heavy paper), laminate, and display.
4. Place the packing peanuts, sponges, pencils, and crayons at each workstation.

Reduce, Reuse, Recycle, Redecorate *(cont.)*

Introduce the Activity

1. Read a book of your choice that reinforces the theme of recycling or taking care of our Earth. (**Suggestions:** *Recycle: A Handbook for Kids* by Gail Gibbons; *Garbage and Recycling* by Rosie Harlow)
2. Introduce the word cards for the unit. Discuss the meaning of new words and concepts.
3. Predict what will happen if you place a packing peanut into the cup of water. Put the packing peanut into the water. Observe and discuss what happens.
   (**Hint:** Stir the water to speed up the dissolving process.)
4. Predict what will happen if you just get part of the packing peanut damp and press it on another packing peanut.
5. Demonstrate this experiment to the entire class. Follow the steps outlined below.

Procedure

1. Place the dampened sponge on a plate.
2. Choose a packing peanut and carefully push one end into the sponge. Then, attach the wet end to another packing peanut.
3. Continue to stick these together creating your own packing peanut "sculptures."

   CAUTION: If the packing peanuts become too wet, they will dissolve into a gooey blob.
4. Add details as desired until your sculpture is complete.
5. Illustrate this experiment on the Science Journal page.

Family Connection

Send home the Family Connection page and ask students to complete it with their families.

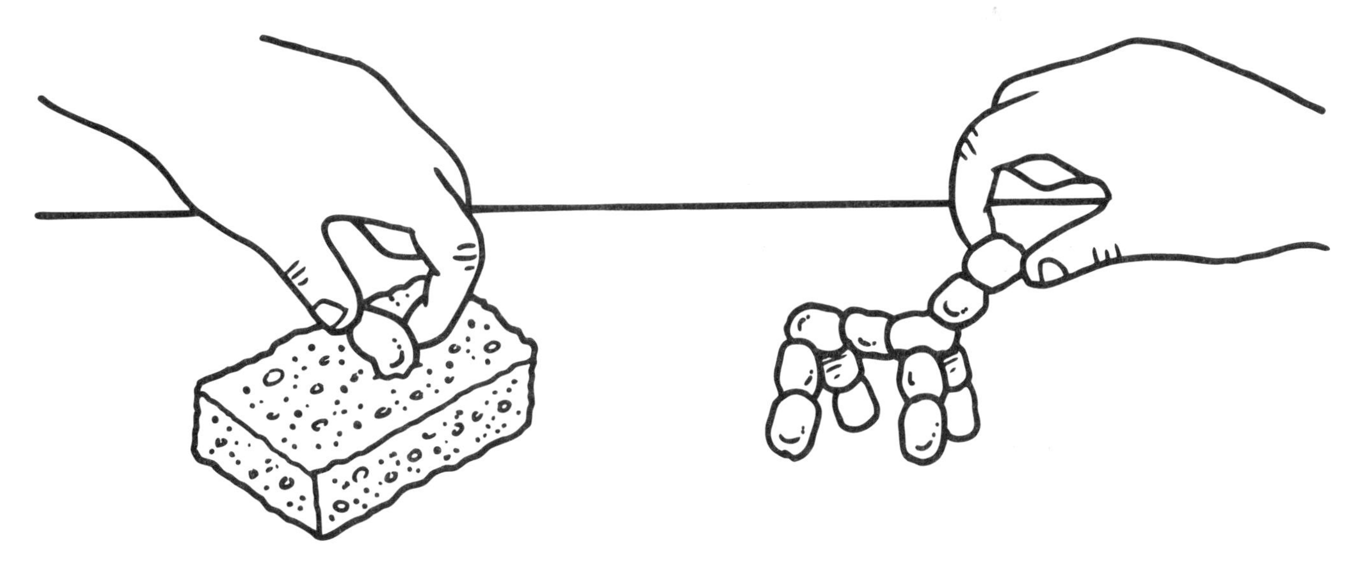

Fun Science Questions and Facts

What are the packing peanuts made of?

They are made of cornstarch, so they will totally dissolve in water and are harmless to our environment.

What if I put a packing peanut in my mouth?

They are harmless and will dissolve in your mouth. However, plain cornstarch isn't very tasty.

Will all packing peanuts work for this experiment?

No, if the packing peanut is made out of Styrofoam, it won't dissolve. A good extension activity is to have some types of packing peanuts mixed together and ask your students to conduct this experiment and identify which are cornstarch (recyclable) and which are Styrofoam (not able to be recycled).

Can I use markers to add details to my sculpture?

Remember that the cornstarch will dissolve when it gets wet, so if you are careful not to get it too wet, you can add details with markers. Toothpicks could also be used to poke holes to add details to sculptures.

Where can I get this type of packing peanut?

Many environmentally friendly companies have switched from Styrofoam to cornstarch packing peanuts. Often the mail service-type stores use the cornstarch packing products. Several of the educational supply companies also carry cornstarch peanuts in a variety of colors and shapes.

How can our class be involved in recycling?

Consider choosing one type of recycling project, such as collecting cans, paper, or plastic bottles, and chart your progress toward a goal. For example: your goal could be to recycle 2,000 pounds of paper, which will save 17 trees.

